Organic Chemistry
Laboratory Manual

Leonard Keller

Joseph Lichter

Lilia San Miguel

Sandra Stojanovic

Department of Chemistry and Biochemistry

Florida International University

macmillan learning
curriculum solutions

Sustainability
Hayden-McNeil's standard paper stock uses a minimum of 30% post-consumer waste. We offer higher % options by request, including a 100% recycled stock. Additionally, Hayden-McNeil Custom Digital provides authors with the opportunity to convert print products to a digital format. Hayden-McNeil is part of a larger sustainability initiative through Macmillan Learning. Visit http://sustainability.macmillan.com to learn more.

bedford/st. martin's • hayden-mcneil
w.h. freeman • worth publishers

Organic Chemistry Laboratory

Table of Contents

Laboratory Glassware

50 mL Round-
bottomed
boiling flask

100 mL Round-
bottomed
boiling flask

250 mL Round-
bottomed
boiling flask

Three-necked
flask

Separatory
funnel

Vacuum adapter

Distillation head

Stopper

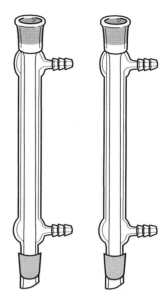

Condenser
(West)

Fractionating
column

Claisen adapter

Thermometer
adapter

Ebulliator
tube

©Hayden-McNeil, LLC

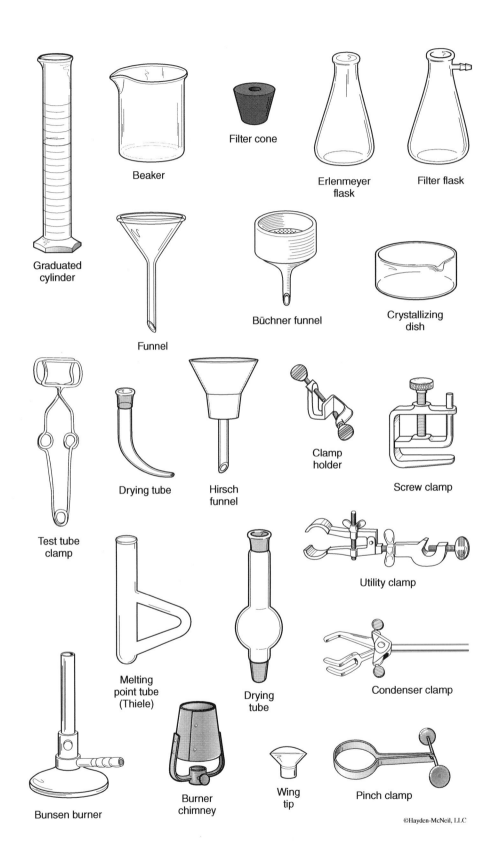

Graduated cylinder

Beaker

Filter cone

Erlenmeyer flask

Filter flask

Funnel

Büchner funnel

Crystallizing dish

Test tube clamp

Drying tube

Hirsch funnel

Clamp holder

Screw clamp

Melting point tube (Thiele)

Drying tube

Utility clamp

Condenser clamp

Bunsen burner

Burner chimney

Wing tip

Pinch clamp

©Hayden-McNeil, LLC

CHM **2210L**

Organic Chemistry I
Laboratory Manual

CHAPTER 1

Keeping the Organic Laboratory Notebook

The laboratory notebook is perhaps *the most valuable laboratory equipment* that you own. With it you should be able to duplicate your work, find out what happened many years later, and even find mistakes made at the time. Since it is meant to be a permanent record, a laboratory notebook should be one with pages that are *bound* and *numbered*. To make the grading procedure easier, the laboratory notebook that you will use also contains duplicate pages with perforations that can be removed and submitted to your instructor at the end of the laboratory period.

Use a ballpoint pen, any color but red. Never erase! Just draw a line through your mistakes. The first page of the notebook should contain your name, student ID number, course and section number, semester taken, and your instructor's name. The second page is a Table of Contents that should be filled out as the experiments are performed. The third page is to be left blank in case more space is needed for the Table of Contents. The experimental work starts on the fourth page.

Each experiment should start on a new page and should indicate the date, name of the experiment, and source. The **purpose** of the experiment follows next. Sometimes an experiment has more than one purpose; if so, specify that fact. The purpose should be short and to the point.

Next comes a brief **introduction** (background information) about the experiment. This *should not* be copied word for word from the introduction given in the laboratory manual. Here is where your lecture material may be useful. Look up information in other books available in the library, and do not forget to cite any references that you use.

If a chemical reaction is involved in the experiment, the reaction equation should be inserted at this point. A reaction mechanism, if known, should also be included.

The next part is the **procedure** itself. Write it in *outline form* so that it will be easy to follow. Use only the left half of the page for the procedure (the other half of the page is used to write observations or data while you are actually performing each step in the laboratory). After the procedure, prepare a **Table of Physical Constants** of the chemicals to be used. The table should include the name of the compound, the formula, formula weight, melting point, boiling point, density, and solubility. *The CRC Handbook of Chemistry and Physics* (available in the laboratory, stockroom, or library) is a good place to get these values. LEARN HOW TO USE THE CRC; IT IS EXTREMELY USEFUL.

All of the above information should be in your notebook before coming to the laboratory. Your instructor will not let you start the experiment if your notebook is not ready.

When performing the experiment, write down all observations: color changes, temperature changes, precipitates formed, etc. When performing a weighing, show a detailed account of the same.

After performing the experiment, the interpretation of the data/observations follows. Here is where the melting/boiling point of the product should be recorded. The calculation of percent yield/recovery should always be done in detail.

The next section should be the conclusion of the experiment. It is here where you should look back at the purpose and evaluate how well you have accomplished it. Remember that the experiments you are performing are going to work most of the time, so avoid the usual cliché of "the experiment went well." Discuss your yield and melting point of the product. Give some explanation as to why they were good or bad. Comment on how you would avoid some problems if you were to perform the experiment a second time, etc.

Finally, if there are any questions at the end of the experiment, this is where they should be answered.

As an example, suppose you are going to prepare 1-bromobutane in the laboratory. Your notebook should look like the example on the following pages.

February 21, 2007

SYNTHESIS OF 1-BROMOBUTANE

Experiment # 5, Ticknor and Gabrielsen, "Organic Chemistry in the Laboratory," Kendall Hunt, 1983, pages 5–9.

Purpose

The purpose of this experiment is to prepare 1-bromobutane. The technique of heating at reflux will be introduced in the process of the preparation.

Introduction

Alkyl halides can be prepared from alcohols by nucleophilic substitution using halide ion in the presence of acid. In this experiment, n-butyl bromide will be prepared by heating 1-butanol with sodium bromide and sulfuric acid. Continuous heating of a mixture at its boiling point is a procedure referred to as "heating at reflux." By arranging a condenser vertically from the neck of a round-bottom flask, a reaction mixture can be heated at its boiling point for an extended period of time without loss of liquid. When the liquid vaporizes, it travels to the condenser where it is cooled, liquefied, and returned to the reaction flask. This technique will be demonstrated in this experiment.

The reaction involved is the following:

$$2 \ CH_3CH_2CH_2CH_2OH + 2 \ NaBr + H_2SO_4 \rightarrow 2 \ CH_3CH_2CH_2CH_2Br + Na_2SO_4 + 2 \ H_2O$$

1. Weigh a 250 mL round-bottom flask and add about 16 mL of 1-butanol. Calculate the weight of 1-butanol used.	**Weight of flask, beaker and alcohol** **233.56 g** **Weight of Flask and beaker** **219.79 g** **Weight of 1-butanol** **13.77 g**
2. Add about 24 g of NaBr and about 25 mL of deionized water to the 1-butanol.	
3. Cool the mixture in an ice water bath to less than 10°C.	**Mixture reached 5°C**
4. Slowly add about 20 mL of concentrated sulfuric acid with swirling.	**The mixture warmed up and turned a yellow color.**
5. Reflux the mixture for about 30 min.	**See page 40 for reflux setup. Mixture darkened as reflux continued.**

6. Let the mixture cool and distill until the distillate is no longer cloudy. Place the receiver used to collect the distillate in an ice water bath, since it is very volatile.	There are 2 layers present in the distillate. They are orange. Instructor said it could be due to some free bromine present.
7. Collect a few drops of clear distillate in a test tube. Add water and shake well. If two layers form, continue distilling for another 5–10 min. and repeat this test. If two layers do not form, distill for another 5–10 minutes.	See page 20 for sample distillation setup. Collected everything that came over up to 100°C. Initially cloudy, white liquid, then clear. After test, I need to distill more.
8. Pour distillate into a separatory funnel.	Water went into upper layer—lower layer is organic product.
9. Wash the distillate with 25 mL of deionized water and separate the organic layer.	Need to take organic layer from the bottom and aqueous from top—throw away.
10. Wash the organic layer with about 25 mL of ice cold conc. H_2SO_4 and separate.	
11. Wash the organic layer with about 15 mL of 10% NaOH solution. Separate the layers.	Clean sep funnel. Put organic layer back in sep funnel. Repeat process.
12. Place the organic layer in a 250 mL Erlenmeyer flask and dry it with anhydrous $MgSO_4$.	
13. Filter by gravity into a dry 50 mL round-bottom flask.	Cloudy product turned clear when $MgSO_4$ added. Corked flask and waited 5min.
14. Distill the dry product and collect the fraction with boiling point range of 101°C (+/–5°) into a pre-weighed, labeled vial.	Actually I decanted instead of filtered. Collected product bp range: 100–103°C
15. Weigh the vial with the product and calculate the weight of product collected.	Weight of vial w/product 36.62 g Weight of vial <u>20.42 g</u> Weight of product 16.20 g

Table of Physical Constants

Name	Formula	M.W.	Density	m.p.	b.p.	Solubility
1-Butanol	$CH_3(CH_2)_3OH$	74.12	0.8098		117.2	H_2O, alcohol, acetone
Sulfuric Acid	H_2SO_4	98.08	1.841	10.4	338	H_2O, dec. alcohol
Sodium Bromide	NaBr	102.9				sol. H_2O; slightly sol. alcohol
1-Bromobutane	$CH_3(CH_2)_3Br$	137.0	1.276	−112	102	alcohol, ether, acet., $CHCl_3$

Calculations:

$$13.377 \text{ g } 1\text{-BuOH} \times \frac{1 \text{ mole } 1\text{-BuOH}}{74.12 \text{ g } 1\text{-BuOH}} = 0.1857 \text{ mole } 1\text{-butanol}$$

$$24 \text{ g NaBr} \times \frac{1 \text{ mole NaBr}}{103 \text{ g NaBr}} = 0.23 \text{ mole NaBr}$$

$$20 \text{ mL conc } H_2SO_4 \times \frac{1.82 \text{ g soln}}{1 \text{ mL conc } H_2SO_4} \times \frac{98 \text{ g } H_2SO_4}{100 \text{ g soln}} \times \frac{1 \text{ mole } H_2SO_4}{98 \text{ g } H_2SO_4} = 0.36 \text{ mole } H_2SO_4$$

Therefore, 1-butanol is the limiting reagent.

$$0.1857 \text{ mol } 1\text{-BuOH} \times \frac{1 \text{ mole } 1\text{-BuBr}}{1 \text{ mol } 1\text{-BuOH}} \times \frac{137 \text{ g } 1\text{-BuBr}}{1 \text{ mole } 1\text{-BuBr}} = 25.4 \text{ g } 1\text{-BuBr Theoretical Yield}$$

Conclusion: This reaction proved to be more difficult than one would have expected by just learning about nucleophilic substitution reactions in lecture class. Keeping the mixture cool enough while adding the sulfuric acid was tricky, and the initial distillation of the product proved difficult because of severe foaming in the distillation flask. It was also hard to tell when to stop distilling. I am not really sure why the yield wasn't higher; there was no obvious loss of material during the workup manipulations. It may just be an inherently low-yielding reaction where side reactions such as alcohol dehydration can compete with alkyl halide formation. My boiling point range of 97°–101°C was quite close to the literature boiling point of 102°C.

Not all of the experiments you will do are of this type. Some of the experiments are designed to let you practice a technique. Consider, for example, the experiment on distillation. The Introduction would contain a statement of the purpose of the experiment.

February 21, 2007

DISTILLATION

Introduction

The purpose of this experiment is to separate two liquids by simple and fractional distillation and to observe the degree of separation by using a graphical method of analysis.

Experimental Procedures and Results

(In your pre-lab write-up, you might wish to sketch the apparatus. If you have been told that you are to record the volume distilled for each 2°C change in temperature, you might wish to plan for a table to record the results as you observe them.)

Procedure

1. Place 15 mL H$_2$O and 15 mL of acetone in a 50 mL round-bottom flask.	Clamp the flask in place and cover it until set up and ready to go.
2. Add three boiling stones.	
3. Assemble simple distillation apparatus using 10 or 25 mL graduated cylinder as receiver. See Figure 9.	Instructor showed us how to use a rubber band to hold connections together.
4. ~~Test heating mantle and variac to see if they perform correctly.~~	Instructor told us to heat slowly and carefully with a Bunsen burner. We don't have this kind of heating equipment.
5. ~~Set variac to about 30 to begin heating.~~	
6. Record temp of first drop of distillate collected as 0 mL. See following table.	Set up graduated cylinder so the volume could easily be read.
7. Record the temperature at 2 mL intervals until temp reaches about 98°.	While distilling, instructor showed us how to pack column for the next part.
8. Cool flask, record volume of residual liquid.	
9. Pack fractionating column.	
10. Assemble fractional distillation apparatus. See Figure 10.	Fractional distillation makes a BIG difference!
11. Use 15 mL H$_2$O and 15 mL acetone. Repeat steps 6, 7, and 8.	

12. Dry the fractional distillation apparatus.	Rinsed apparatus with acetone and dried.
13. Obtain 30 mL of unknown acetone-water mixture.	
14. Repeat fractional distillation as before.	It was obvious from the data that the unknown was about 68% acetone in water. See table below.
15. Plot temp vs. volume of distillate for each of the distillations.	
16. Determine percent composition of the unknown.	
17. Turn in notebook and graphs.	Experiment complete 4:10 PM 2/21/07

Volume of Distillate (mL) vs. Temperature

mL Collected	0	2	4	6	8	10	12	14	16	18	20	22	24	26
Simple distillation 1:1 mixture	57	59	59	60	60	61	63	90	98	11 mL residue				
Fractional distillation 1:1 mixture	56	56	56	56	56	56	56	58	98	10 mL residue				
Fractional distillation unknown	56	56	56	56	57	57	57	57	57	57	57	98		

Discussion

Extrapolation of the graph shows that the 1:1 mixture is a little over 50% and the unknown is close to 68% acetone. The instructor told us that the unknown was actually 70% acetone.

The table of results should be followed by a normal discussion and any pertinent references (see above).

Table of Physical Constants

Name	Formula	M.W.	Density	m.p.	b.p.	Solubility
Acetone	$(CH_3)_2CO$	58.1	0.789	-95	56.2	H_2O, alcohol, ether, benzene
Water	H_2O	18.0	1.000	0	100	—

Conclusion: Distillation is not so easy a procedure as it sounds. It took an especially long time to set up the apparatus so that it would work properly. Heating at the correct rate in order to avoid flooding of the fractionating column was also tricky. It is clear from the graph of my results that fractional distillation is a better procedure for cleanly separating a mixture of volatile liquids than is simple distillation. Even so, there was still a large portion of the mixture that did not completely separate. The problem, however, is that it is more difficult and time consuming to do it properly.

As you can see, the write-up of the experiments will vary with the type of experiment. If you want a general criterion for your notebook, let it be this: keep a notebook with the assumption that you may someday want to repeat any experiment without the benefit of a lab manual. In other words, keep a notebook that would allow you to repeat any experiment from your own notes. Tell what you did, how you did it, and what you obtained or what you learned. A word of caution about the foregoing examples: the results of those experiments are not intended to be guidelines for your results. Those results were made up simply to illustrate how they can be presented and are not intended as hard and fast data.

CHAPTER 2

Physical Properties of Organic Molecules

Organic chemists classify and identify compounds by measuring or observing their physical properties and their chemical properties.

Properties that do *not* change the chemical or structural nature of a substance are referred to as **physical properties**. Properties that *do* change the chemical or structural nature of a substance are referred to as **chemical properties**.

The determination of a compound's physical properties can be useful in several different ways. Physical properties can be used (1) in structure determination, (2) to determine the purity of a substance, and (3) if it is not pure, to determine how to separate contaminating substances from a compound.

The most common physical properties of interest to organic chemists are color, odor, crystalline form (if it is a solid), refractive index (if it is a liquid), density, solubility in various solvents, melting point (for solids), adsorptivity, and boiling point (for liquids). Another class of physical properties is referred to as **spectroscopic properties**. These properties come about by the interaction of a substance with electromagnetic radiation.

In the first part of this course, you will learn how to measure and use melting point, boiling point, solubility, and differential adsorptivity to identify and purify organic solids and liquids. In the second semester, you will learn how to use two forms of spectroscopy (infrared and nuclear magnetic resonance) to determine the chemical structure of organic compounds.

Part 1: Melting Point

INTRODUCTION

Melting point is a physical property that can be used to determine (1) the identity and (2) the purity of an organic solid.

The melting point of a solid is the characteristic temperature at which the solid and liquid states are in equilibrium.

Melting point determination is one of the simplest and yet most important methods of identifying organic solids. Most organic solids melt in the convenient range of 50° to 250°C. This is in striking contrast to inorganic substances that, for the most part, melt at much higher temperatures (300° to 1500°).

Since the melting point of a solid is a characteristic and easily determined property, it can be used as partial evidence of a substance's identity. However, because many organic compounds possess the same melting point, the absolute identity of a substance cannot be determined by melting point alone.

Pure organic solids usually melt sharply (that is, over a very narrow temperature range). However, because a laboratory melting point apparatus has less than perfect heat transfer, a **melting point range** rather than a single temperature is obtained even for pure substances. The melting point range is usually no greater than two degrees for a pure substance when using the apparatus available in most elementary organic laboratories. Whereas a pure substance melts sharply, a mixture of compounds (such as an impure substance) melts over a wide range. This is true even though the components of the mixture may individually melt at the same temperature. For example, both urea and cinnamic acid melt at 135°C. A mixture of the two may begin melting as low as 100°C and melt over a 15° to 20°C range. Generally, a mixture of two substances will melt lower than either of the two substances alone. This is due to a physical phenomenon called "freezing/melting point depression." This generality allows us to use the melting point *range* as a rough criterion for the purity of a sample: *melting point range increases as purity decreases.*

A "mixed melting point" determination can establish the identity or nonidentity of two similarly melting compounds.

Note that many compounds decompose rather than melt, and, although decomposition temperatures can be highly reproducible, decomposition can complicate the determination of the true melting point. Decomposition may be evidenced by a change in color of the solid, gas evolution, or a melting and resolidification due to formation of a new compound or a different crystal structure with a higher melting point. Be on the lookout for these, and be sure to record such observations.

GENERAL PROCEDURES FOR THE DETERMINATION OF THE MELTING POINT

There are a number of types of apparatus marketed for the determination of melting point, but they have features in common. Your instructor will demonstrate the use of the instrument or instruments available in your laboratory. In the more common procedure, the clean, dry solid is carefully crushed and introduced into a thin-walled capillary tube produced for just this purpose. Only a very small amount of solid is needed, and, in rare cases where this is all of the sample that exists, it can even be recovered. The tube is now heated. The tube can be heated in a bath of oil (*e.g.*, in a Thiele tube) using a Bunsen burner as the heat source. By attaching the tube directly to a thermometer so that the compound is directly adjacent to the thermometer bulb, the melting point temperature can be measured quite accurately. The Mel-Temp apparatus has an electrically heated block that contains the thermometer bulb and capillary tube.

Whichever apparatus is available, the following points are relevant:

1. The compound must be dry; otherwise, it may dissolve in residual solvent rather than truly melt.

2. The temperature must be raised slowly. This allows for good heat transfer and assures that the sample and the thermometer are at the same temperature. Heating slowly also assures you that you are recording the narrowest range. If you know the approximate melting point of the compound, heat the sample rapidly until it is about 10° below the expected melting point and heat thereafter at 2° per minute.

    If the material is totally unfamiliar to you, prepare two samples. Do one melting point quickly by heating the sample 15° to 20° per minute until melting is observed. Allow the apparatus to cool to 10° below this point, and heat the fresh sample at a rate of 2° per minute to obtain the correct melting point range.

3. Always report two temperatures, the first being where the sample begins to melt (*i.e.*, when the first bit of liquid can be observed), and the second being where the sample has completely melted. Remember that softening or a shrinking of the sample does not constitute melting. You must see liquid.

    Record all observations in your laboratory notebook. For example, "The compound melts sharply at 143.5–144°C," or "The compound decomposes with considerable darkening at 218–223°C." Include the literature value of the melting point for the compound if it is a known substance.

    You will find melting points and boiling points listed in reference books where a single temperature is listed. It is possible to measure these physical constants with very high accuracy, but this is not likely to occur in a student teaching laboratory. You will be reporting data as a range.

4. Melting points should be determined during the class period, but can be performed at any time when the main laboratory is open and an instructor is present.

SPECIFIC PROCEDURE

In this experiment you will be using the Mel-Temp apparatus to determine the melting point *range* of solids. Your instructor will show you how to use this device properly. After learning how to prepare the sample for melting point determination, obtain a sample of pure urea, m.p. 134–136°C, and determine its melting point. *Always find the melting point in duplicate trials.* Repeat the procedure, this time using benzoic acid, m.p. 121–123°C. When you feel comfortable with the procedure, obtain an unknown and determine its melting point. Check your results with your instructor.

Do the following exercises in your notebook:

Questions

1. In the determination of a melting point, why is it necessary to:

    a. use a powdered rather than a crystalline sample?

    b. use a new capillary tube for each determination?

    c. not heat the sample too rapidly near the melting point?

2. The melting point of a pure unknown compound was found to be 95.4°C. The unknown was thought to be one of three known compounds, samples of which were all available. Describe a procedure for identifying the unknown as one of the three known compounds.

3. Which has a lower freezing point: ice or ice cream? Why?

Part 2: Boiling Point

INTRODUCTION

When a liquid is kept in a sealed container, some of the molecules escape from the surface into the space above it, and equilibrium is established as the number of molecules that escape become equal in number to the molecules that return to the liquid surface. The molecules in the vapor phase strike the walls of the container and exert a pressure which is defined as the **vapor pressure of the liquid.**

The vapor pressure of a liquid rises steadily as the temperature is increased. If a liquid is in an open container, then the temperature at which the vapor pressure of the liquid is equal to the atmospheric pressure is called the **boiling point** of the liquid. At a given atmospheric pressure, the boiling point is a characteristic physical property of a pure liquid.

There are two methods available to determine the boiling point of a volatile liquid. If large quantities of material are available, one simply records the boiling point shown on the thermometer as the substance distills during a simple distillation (Figure 3-3). With smaller amounts of material, a microdetermination of the boiling point can be effected using the apparatus shown in Figure 2-1.

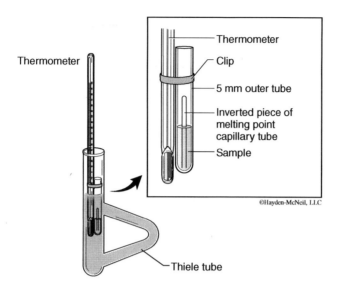

Figure 2-1.

In today's experiment you will learn how to determine the boiling point of a volatile liquid using the microboiling point apparatus, first by determining the boiling point of a known substance and then by determining the boiling point of an unknown substance.

MICROBOILING POINT DETERMINATION

The technique described below for determining the boiling point of an organic liquid has the advantage of being applicable to small amounts of material. This microtechnique utilizes a melting point capillary inverted in a length of 5 mm glass tubing, which in turn is attached to a thermometer and is placed in a Thiele tube (see Figure 2-1).

Procedure

Put a few drops of liquid into a 5 mm glass tube, which will serve as the sample holder. Fasten this tube to the thermometer using the special metal clip that will be provided. Adjust the tube so that the bottoms of the tube and the thermometer bulb are at the same height. Put a 6–7 cm long melting point capillary tube *with the sealed end up* into the 5 mm sample holder tube. Suspend the entire assembly in the Thiele tube—placing it at a level such that the oil in the Thiele tube will not run into the 5 mm tube and contaminate the sample. Keep in mind that the oil will expand when it is heated—and that its level will therefore rise.

Heat the oil at the elbow of the Thiele tube until bubbles emerge rapidly and continuously from the capillary and from its submerged tip. Be sure the bubbles are rapidly being produced. At that point, stop heating and soon the bubbles will slow down and eventually stop. When they stop, the liquid will reenter the capillary tube. Record the temperature the moment when the liquid reenters the capillary tube. This is the boiling point of the liquid.

After recording the boiling point, let the apparatus cool to 20 degrees below the boiling point, and then repeat the process in order to gather a second measurement. These two results should be averaged.

The theory behind the boiling point determination is that air initially trapped in the capillary tube expands during heating and escapes, evidenced by the initial slow bubble formation. At the same time vapor from the liquid enters the capillary tube displacing the air. At the boiling point of the liquid, the pressure inside the capillary will be equal to atmospheric pressure. As the temperature rises just above the boiling point, the vapor will start to escape causing rapid bubble formation. Once you stop heating the tube, the vapor in the capillary will lower in pressure. As it reaches atmospheric pressure, liquid will be drawn into the capillary tube. The temperature at which the liquid reenters is the boiling point. In theory, the temperature when rapid bubble formation occurs is also the boiling point but is more difficult to experimentally measure.

Repeating the process a second and/or third time will ensure an accurate determination of the boiling point. The experimenter must be careful not to boil away or evaporate too much of the liquid in the tube. If so, more liquid sample can be added to the test tube.

Practice this technique using a sample of ethanol, b.p. 78°C. Then obtain an unknown liquid and determine its boiling point. Do at least two determinations, as you did with the melting point unknown. Check your results with your instructor.

Questions

1. Why is it necessary to position the sample tube right next to the thermometer bulb in the Thiele tube?

2. The normal boiling point of benzene is 80°C. What is the vapor pressure of benzene at 80°C?

3. Define boiling point. How does this definition describe what is occurring in micro-boiling point determination method; *i.e.*, that the boiling point is the temperature at which the liquid levels inside and outside of the capillary tube are the same?

Part 3: Solubility Properties of Organic Solids

INTRODUCTION

Solubility may be defined as the ability for a given substance, the solute, to dissolve in a solvent. The term also refers to the degree to which a substance dissolves in a solvent to make a solution (often expressed as grams of solute per liter of solvent). Generally, the solubility of solids in liquids increases with temperature.

When a solid dissolves in a liquid, a change in the physical state of the solid takes place. Heat is therefore required to overcome the bonds that hold together the molecules in the solid. At the same time, heat is given off during the formation of new solute-to-solvent interactions.

Knowledge of the solubility of a substance is significant in three ways. Since it is almost always necessary to work with a compound in solution, one must either know, or be able to predict, whether the substance will dissolve in water, aqueous acid or base, or organic solvents. Second, if the molecular structure of a compound is not known, its solubility characteristics can serve as one basis for deducing its structure. Third, in order to perform a *recrystallization*, one of the most important techniques for the purification of solids, the solubility properties of the solid in question must be determined. For recrystallization, a solid should be sparingly soluble in the recrystallizing solvent at room temperature and yet be quite soluble at the boiling point of the solvent selected. This concept will be covered in detail in a later experiment.

Although there are no simple rules that can be used to predict the solubility of a given substance in a solvent, there are some generalizations that, along with sufficient laboratory experience, may serve as a basis for an educated guess. The solubility of organic compounds is to a large degree a function of the polarities of both the solvent and the solute. A general rule is that "like dissolves like." That is, polar solvents dissolve polar compounds and nonpolar solvents dissolve nonpolar compounds. Usually, compounds having a functional group that can form hydrogen bonds (*e.g.*, –OH, –NH, –COOH, –CONRH) will be more soluble in hydroxylic solvents (those containing –OH groups) than in hydrocarbon solvents such as toluene and hexane. However, if the functional group is not a major part of the molecule, the solubility behavior may be reversed (*e.g.*, dodecyl alcohol, $CH_3(CH_2)_{10}CH_2OH$, is almost insoluble in water because its twelve-carbon chain makes it behave more like a hydrocarbon than an alcohol).

SOLUBILITY DETERMINATION

General Procedures for Testing Solubility

Crush the solid finely between two pieces of weighing paper or filter paper using your spatula. Place a few crystals of the solid in a clean, dry test tube. Add 1–2 mL of the solvent (approximately 25–35 drops) to be tested and shake the mixture. If no appreciable disappearance of solid is noted, place the test tube in a water bath (a beaker of warm water). The temperature of the water bath should not be more than a few degrees above the boiling point of the solvent. Continue to shake the mixture until the solvent begins to boil. Caution—bumping may occur when heating small amounts of material in a test tube. If the solid dissolves, remove the test tube from the water bath and allow it to cool. Immerse the test tube in an ice bath and note if recrystallization occurs. If, when the solvent is boiling, some but not all of the solid appears to have dissolved, add an additional 1–2 drops of solvent and reheat. If additional material dissolves, add a third portion of solvent. If some of the compound still remains undissolved, the compound is either only very slightly soluble in the hot solvent and too much solvent would be required to recrystallize it, or an insoluble impurity may be present.

When recording the results of the solubility tests in your notebook, use commonly accepted abbreviations for your observations. A substance that is insoluble is designated **I**, meaning no appreciable disappearance of solid was noted. A substance that is soluble, **S**, disappears to produce a homogeneous solution. If you believe that only some of the solid has dissolved, you should conclude that the substance is partially soluble, **PS**. If you believe that a substance is only *very slightly soluble*, use the symbol **δ**. Note that if the solid has a melting point below the boiling point of the solvent being tested, it may melt while you are determining the solubility in hot solvent. You might mistake this for solubility. Therefore, watch for immiscible globules of melted organic solid floating on the surface of the solvent or circulating through it if stirred vigorously. Finally, in those cases where you think a solid is **PS**, check this assumption by adding a second portion of hot solvent. This should reduce the bulk of the solid by about the same amount as the first portion of solvent did. If this does not happen, the possibility that an insoluble impurity is present should be suspected.

SPECIFIC PROCEDURE

In this part of the experiment, you will use some common organic solids and solvents and compare their solubilities with the solubility of an ionic solid, NaCl. The solids and solvents that will be used are shown below. The solvents are listed in order of increasing polarity.

SOLIDS	SOLVENTS (listed in the order of increasing polarity)
NaCl	C_6H_{14} (hexane) - *least polar*
NH_2CONH_2 (urea)	$C_6H_5CH_3$ (toluene)
C_6H_5COOH (benzoic acid)	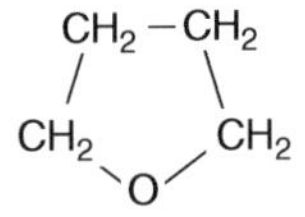 (THF)
$C_{10}H_8$ (naphthalene)	
	$CH_3CO_2CH_2CH_3$ (ethyl acetate)
	CH_3CH_2OH (ethyl alcohol)
	H_2O (water) - *most polar*

Test each solid separately with the six different solvents. Place a small amount of solid (about 0.1 gram) in each of six test tubes. Add about 2 mL of a different solvent to each test tube. Determine the solubility of the solid in each solvent. SHAKE WELL BEFORE

ARRIVING AT ANY CONCLUSIONS. Determine if the solid is insoluble (I), partially soluble (PS), or soluble (S).

Place a beaker with water on a hot plate and heat the water to about 40–50°C. Place those test tubes that you decided contain insoluble or partially soluble solid in the hot water bath, and determine their solubility at the higher temperature.

In your notebook, prepare a table of your results as shown below. Use each block as a fraction: the numerator will show the solubility in cold solvent, and the denominator will show the solubility in the hot solvent. A sample setup (for aspirin and some common solvents) is shown below:

Solvent → Solute	Hexane	THF	Ethyl Alcohol	Ethyl Acetate	Water
Aspirin	I / I	δ / 2×PS	I / PS3×S	PS / S	I / δ

I = insoluble, nothing is missing

δ = very slightly soluble, almost imperceptible

PS = partially soluble, material seems to have been reduced over its original amount

S = soluble, all solid gone

v = very

2×, 3×, etc. = followed by an observation such as PS or I, indicates additional mLs of solvent were added to confirm a suspected observation

NOTE: *Be sure to dispose of all substances used in the appropriate waste containers, not in the sink.*

After determining that a solute is soluble in a particular hot solvent, let the test tube cool to room temperature and observe if any recrystallization takes place. Record your observations in your notebook.

Do the following exercises in your notebook:

Questions

1. According to your results, list the solids tested in order of increasing polarity—starting with the least polar and finishing with the most polar. Explain how you arrived at your conclusions.

2. Did any of the solutes recrystallize when the solvent was cooled? List the solute(s) and the solvent(s) where this occurred.

3. What criteria make a solvent satisfactory for recrystallization?

CHAPTER 3

Distillation

INTRODUCTION

Distillation is a method that can be used to purify volatile liquids—either by separating them from nonvolatile materials or from other volatile substances. The process involves heating the impure liquid to its boiling point (defined below), cooling the vapor until it reliquifies (condenses), and collecting the condensate. If the impurities are not volatile, they will be left behind, and only the pure, volatile liquid will distill over. If, however, the impurities are volatile, a separation can occur by virtue of the difference in the boiling points of the various volatile components of the mixture.

The vapor pressure of a liquid increases with an increase in temperature. The **boiling point** of a pure liquid is the temperature at which the vapor pressure equals atmospheric pressure. If a mixture of two miscible liquids with different boiling points is heated until it boils, the vapor will not have the same composition as the liquid. It will be more concentrated in the more volatile component. Simply stated, Raoult's Law says that the partial pressure of each component will be equal to the vapor pressure of the pure component multiplied by the mole fraction of that component in the mixture. For miscible liquids, then:

$$P_{total} = P_a^o N_a + P_b^o N_b$$

where P_a^o and P_b^o are the vapor pressures of the pure substances a and b, and N_a and N_b are the respective mole fractions of a and b. Distillation is the technique that takes advantage of these physical properties, and it is used for both purification (separation from impurities) and determination of boiling point (identification).

SIMPLE DISTILLATION

Consider Figure 3-1, which illustrates the behavior of a mixture of A and B, two miscible, volatile liquids with boiling points T_A and T_B, respectively. The lower of the two solid curves represents the boiling point of any mixture of A and B. The upper curve represents the composition of the vapor in equilibrium with the liquid. At 100% A or 100% B, the curves meet, because pure-boiling A (at T_A) can only be in equilibrium with pure A vapor; the same applies to pure B (at T_B). If a mixture of A and B with composition C_1 is heated, it will boil at T_{C1} and the vapor will have the composition given by C_2. This means that if C_1 were placed in a distillation apparatus and heated to its boiling point, the vapor (and, therefore, the first drop of liquid to be condensed) would have the composition C_2; *i.e.*, it would be much richer in A, the more volatile of the two components, than was the original liquid. As the distillation proceeds, component A would be selectively removed from the liquid. The composition of the liquid would change gradually from C_1 to 100% B. The boiling point of the liquid would gradually rise from T_{C1} to T_B; at the same time, the composition of the distillate would gradually change from C_2 (rich in A) to 100% B. Thus, in a simple distillation of a two-component mixture, the first material to distill (sometimes called the first cut or first fraction) will be rich in the more volatile component, and the second material to distill (last cut or fraction) will be rich in the less volatile or higher boiling component.

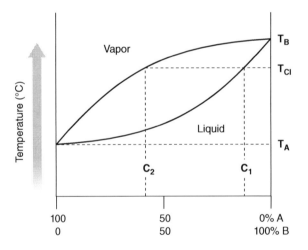

Figure 3-1. *Diagram of Liquid-Vapor Composition During Simple Distillation.*

From a practical point of view, **simple distillation** is used to separate a volatile liquid from either (1) nonvolatile impurities or (2) from another liquid whose boiling point is *at least 80° higher* than that of the first. *It is not possible to use simple distillation to completely separate a mixture of two volatile liquids whose boiling points are too close together.* While the vapor obtained in distilling such a mixture will be richer in the lower boiling (more volatile) component, it will still contain a significant amount of the higher boiling component. Three types of temperature behavior that occur during simple distillation are shown in Figure 3-2.

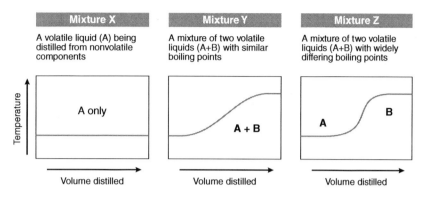

Good separations are achieved in X and Z

Figure 3-2.

The apparatus for a simple distillation setup is shown in Figure 3-3.

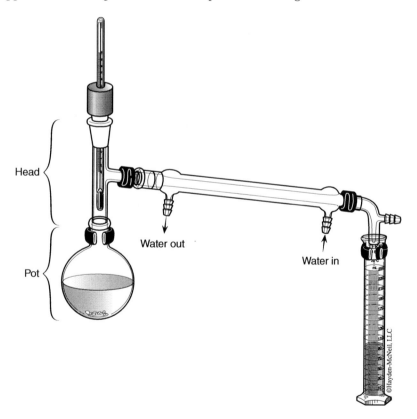

Figure 3-3. Apparatus for Simple Distillation.

FRACTIONAL DISTILLATION

In principle, one way to use simple distillation to separate two volatile components with a boiling point difference of less than 80° would be to do successive, simple distillations; *i.e.*, redistilling the fraction from the previous distillation that is richer in the more volatile component. Fortunately, there is an alternative to such a tedious and time-consuming procedure. It is referred to as **fractional distillation**. With fractional distillation, the repeated distillations are accomplished almost automatically in a single process. The apparatus for fractional distillation is shown in Figure 3-4. A vertical column, which is packed with some inert material such as glass beads or glass helices, is inserted between the distilling flask and the condenser. The increased surface area in the column allows some of the hot vapor to condense as it rises through the column. It then falls back into the distilling flask, is revaporized, and the more volatile components proceed up the column once again.

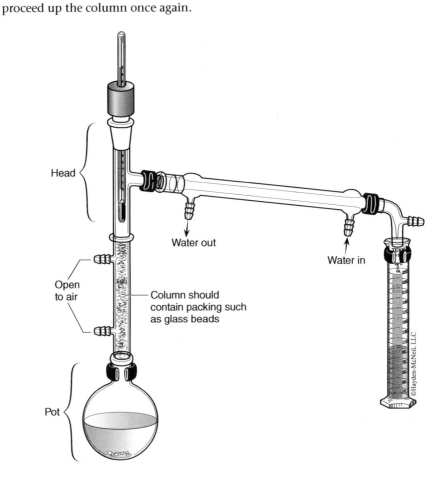

Figure 3-4. *Apparatus for Fractional Distillation.*

Figure 3-5 illustrates the process graphically. The original A-B mixture with composition C_1 boils at temperature T_{C1}, and the vapors enter the column at that temperature. If they condense in the column, the condensate will have the composition C_2. This vaporizes near the bottom of the column at temperature T_{C2}, producing vapors with composition C_3. These may condense further up the column at T_{C3}; vaporization now gives vapor with composition C_4, etc. If the column is sufficiently long, *i.e.*, if it produces enough successive vaporizations and condensations, the distillate that comes over will be nearly pure A. This will continue until all of A is removed, after which the temperature will rise to the boiling point of B.

This series of repeated condensations and revaporizations amounts to a number of simple distillations occurring *within the column*, with the vapor phase produced in each step becoming richer in the more volatile component. The liquid left behind, meanwhile, becomes richer in the less volatile component. If the column is long enough, this process is repeated many times, and the distillate will consist of the lower boiling component of the mixture in nearly pure form. Using the technique of fractional distillation can therefore effect good separations of volatile components with similar boiling points. While in practice, distilling columns are not 100% efficient; there are columns that have been designed to separate liquids that boil as little as 2° apart.

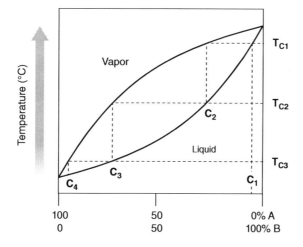

Figure 3-5. *Diagram of Liquid-Vapor Composition for a Fractionating Column.*

The measure of column efficiency in a fractional distillation is described in "theoretical plates." The greater the number of theoretical plates, the better the separation. This is referred to as HETP (Height Equivalent to a Theoretical Plate). A theoretical plate is that portion of the column length required to accomplish one vaporization–condensation step.

THE EXPERIMENT

In this experiment, you will be performing both simple and fractional distillations on a mixture of volatile liquids and will be analyzing the differences between the two separation methods. You will learn how to use your standard-tapered ground glass equipment for the first time. In using this glassware, it is extremely important that the joints be clean. A *very thin film* of stopcock grease is used to ensure a snug fit. It also prevents these joints from becoming "frozen together." Follow your instructor's demonstration on how to grease joints. When disassembling the apparatus, clean the grease from the joints with a paper towel *before* you wet them.

Procedure

Although each student will analyze the data collected from both the simple and the fractional distillation, the instructor will assign each student *either* a simple distillation *or* a fractional distillation to perform. Be sure, however, *to get the data of the part that you did not do* from another student before you leave the laboratory. Otherwise, you will not be able to complete your report.

Part A: Simple Distillation

Assemble the apparatus for simple distillation as shown in Figure 3-3. Obtain a 100 mL heating mantle and rheostat; be sure that they work. Place 10 mL of cyclohexane and 10 mL of toluene into a 100 mL round-bottom flask (round-bottom flasks are filled only halfway). Add 2–3 boiling chips or "boileezers." It is advisable to assemble your apparatus in an end-to-end fashion with respect to the sink in order to maximize the distance between the heat source, the volatile distillate, and the cooling water source. Pay special attention to where the thermometer bulb is positioned. Placement either too high or too low will lead to incorrect temperature readings. Use a graduated cylinder as your receiver since you will be recording the volume of distillate collected.

> **NOTE:** *A word of explanation about the "boiling chip" or boiling stone as it is sometimes called. When a liquid is heated near its boiling point, it can resist boiling for some time and become overheated. A violent eruption releases the excess heat in the form of a large amount of vapor. This is called* **bumping***. The boiling stone provides a nucleation surface for the formation of bubbles and thus leads to smooth boiling. NEVER add a boiling stone to an already-hot solution, as it may induce a severe bump.*

Before starting the distillation procedure, be sure your instructor has checked your setup and has given you the OK to begin. Distill the mixture slowly (1–2 drops/sec.). Avoid temperature fluctuations. Record the temperature when the liquid starts to boil and when the first drops of distillate are collected. Collect the distillate while recording the head temperature versus volume at 1 mL intervals. Stop the distillation when the residual liquid in the distilling flask is about 5–6 mL. In other words, *stop the distillation before the distilling flask dries out!*

Record the barometric pressure (given on the board) in your notebook.

Use graph paper and plot the temperature observed (y-axis) versus volume of distillate collected (x-axis).

Part B: Fractional Distillation

Assemble the apparatus for fractional distillation as shown in Figure 3-4. The fractionating column should be packed with a material designated by your instructor. The packing material should be inert and loosely packed. Make sure that the thermometer bulb does not touch the packing material. Insulate the column by wrapping it in glass wool or aluminum foil. Then follow the instructions given in Part A.

Using the same graph paper from Part A, plot the temperature obtained (y-axis) versus the volume of distillate collected (x-axis). Use different symbols or different colored ink to distinguish simple distillation data from fractional distillation data.

Results: From your graphs of the boiling point versus the volume of distillate collected, compare how effectively the mixture of cyclohexane and toluene was separated by simple distillation and by fractional distillation.

Questions

1. Was there a difference between the head temperature when the liquid first started to boil and the temperature when the first portion of distillate was collected? Explain.

2. What would be the effect of having the thermometer above the side arm of the three-way collecting tube?

3. If two miscible liquids are each found to boil at exactly the same temperature, could you safely conclude that they are identical? Why?

4. What is the purpose of the boiling chips?

5. How would the observed temperature be affected if a distillation were performed on the top of a mountain? Explain.

6. Why should water enter a condenser at the lowest point and leave at the highest point?

CHAPTER 4

Recrystallization

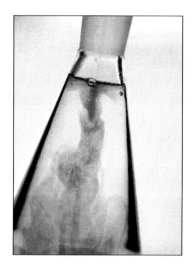

INTRODUCTION

Products from organic reactions are rarely pure when they are first obtained. They contain side products, unconsumed reactants, and other impurities that must be removed. If the product is a solid and the amounts of the impurities are not very large, the product can frequently be purified by a process called **recrystallization**. In this technique, a hot solution containing the compound is slowly cooled, and crystals of the purified compound are *slowly* and selectively precipitated. The procedure works because the impurities either remain dissolved in the solvent or are removed before cooling by filtration or adsorption on Norit (decolorizing carbon). Suction filtration then allows the crystals of the purified material to be collected.

The solvent that is selected to do the job must have one of the following characteristics: it must either (1) dissolve the major component but not the contaminant, (2) dissolve the contaminant but not the major component, or (3) dissolve both but allow the major component to selectively recrystallize upon cooling a hot saturated solution of the material. Often a combination of these characteristics is encountered. Ideally, one looks for a solvent in which the major component dissolves when the solvent is hot and recrystallizes upon cooling.

The general steps for any recrystallization are as follows:

1. Select a proper solvent.

2. Heat the solvent to its boiling point.

3. Dissolve the solid compound in the *minimum amount* of the boiling solvent.

4. Add decolorizing carbon if necessary.

5. Filter the hot mixture through a heated wide-stem or stemless funnel to remove the decolorizing carbon and any insoluble impurities. (This step may be omitted if not applicable.)

6. Allow the hot solution to cool *slowly* to room temperature or lower.

7. If crystals do not appear, the side of the flask is scratched with a glass rod, the solution is cooled further, or a seed crystal of product is added to promote crystallization.

8. The crystals are collected by suction filtration, using a Büchner or Hirsch funnel.

9. The crystals are rinsed with a *small amount of cold solvent.*

10. The crystals are dried.

11. If worthwhile, a second crop of crystals is obtained.

These steps will now be considered in detail.

1. Selection of Solvent

The selection of a proper solvent is vitally important in any recrystallization. A desirable solvent is one in which the product will be very soluble at high temperatures, but only slightly or sparingly soluble at room temperature or lower.

If the substance is known, then the proper solvent can usually be found in the literature. For new compounds, the general rule that "like dissolves like" is valuable. Polar solutes would thus be more likely to dissolve in polar solvents, such as water or 95% ethanol, and less likely to dissolve in nonpolar solvents, such as cyclohexane or ligroin (a mixture of isomeric hexanes). For nonpolar solutes, the opposite solubility characteristics apply.

Usually a solute is polar when it is either ionic or when a functional group, such as $-OH$, $-NH_2$, $-COOH$, and $-NHCOCH_3$, comprises a large portion of the molecule. Solubility in water and alcohol usually results from the formation of hydrogen bonds between these functional groups and the solvent. As the proportion of one of these functional groups in a molecule decreases and the hydrocarbon portion increases, the solute becomes less soluble in polar solvents and more soluble in less polar and nonpolar solvents.

Some characteristics to look for in a good recrystallizing solvent are:

a. The solid to be recrystallized is insoluble in cold solvent but very soluble in boiling solvent.

b. Impurities are either insoluble in boiling solvent or moderately soluble in cold solvent.

c. The solvent should have a boiling point in the range 60° to 110° so that it will not boil away too quickly, yet will allow the crystals to dry rapidly after filtration.

d. The solvent should not react chemically with the substance to be recrystallized.

It is always desirable to strive for the ideal in the first three characteristics, but it is mandatory that the fourth requirement be met.

The choice of the best possible solvent is often a matter of trial and error. An experienced chemist, however, is usually able to select one after only a few trials.

SOLUBILITY TESTING PROCEDURE

First, review the experiment that you did previously on solubility. Of course, you may skip this section if you know what solvent to use for a given recrystallization.

To discover the best solvent for recrystallizing a new compound, place approximately 20 mg (a small spatula tip full) of the compound in a 10 × 75 mm test tube. Add about 0.5 mL of the possible solvent at room temperature while stirring, and note the solubility. If most or all of the compound dissolves, then the solvent is unsatisfactory, since too much of the compound is being lost to the solvent. If only a small part of the compound, however, appears to dissolve, then the solvent may be satisfactory. Place the test tube in a water bath (or a beaker of warm water) and observe how much of the compound dissolves in the hot or boiling solvent. The temperature of the water bath should not be more than a few degrees above the boiling point of the solvent. If the amount that dissolves is small or moderate, the solvent is again unsatisfactory. But if most or all of the compound dissolves, a good recrystallization solvent has likely been found. If necessary, add a small amount of additional solvent to attain complete solution; then allow the test tube to cool slowly, and compare the quantity and size of the resulting crystals with the original material. If necessary, induce crystallization by adding a crystal of the original material to "seed" the cooled solution. The inside of the test tube near the bottom may also be carefully rubbed with a glass stirring rod to induce crystallization.

Sometimes the product being isolated will be too soluble in some solvents and not soluble enough in others. In this case, a mixture of solvents can be useful. For example, suppose that the product is very soluble in ethanol but not very soluble in water. One would then dissolve the product in the minimum amount of hot ethanol, and hot water would be added *slowly* until crystallization or turbidity occurred. Additional hot ethanol would then be added *slowly* until complete solution was again attained, and the solution would be allowed to cool slowly.

When selecting a solvent, avoid any liquid whose boiling point is higher than the melting point of the compound being recrystallized. Otherwise, the solid may melt in the solvent and may then "oil out." This is undesirable because the oil will often be an excellent solvent for impurities, and when the oil finally freezes, the impurities that are dissolved in the oil will be embedded in the crystals.

2. Preparation of the Solution

After selection of the proper solvent, a solution saturated with the substance to be purified is prepared AT THE BOILING POINT OF THE SOLVENT. Solid is added to an Erlenmeyer flask (never a beaker) containing a boiling chip, and the solvent is added in portions as boiling is maintained. If a flammable solvent is used, a steam bath or hot plate MUST be employed; *never a flame.* Add enough solvent so that the material to be purified just dissolves while the solvent is boiling. *Be sure to add only the minimum amount of the boiling solvent needed to dissolve the compound.* This ensures that the solution, when cooled, will return the maximum possible yield of crystals. Be patient; organic compounds often do not dissolve instantaneously. Therefore, extra portions of solvent should *not* be added too quickly. It is also possible that the compound being recrystallized may contain some insoluble impurities. For both of these reasons, too much solvent may needlessly be added in a futile attempt at complete dissolution.

*NOTE: A word of explanation about the "boiling chip" or boiling stone, as it is sometimes called, is in order here. When a liquid is heated near its boiling point, it can resist boiling for some time and become overheated. A violent eruption releases the excess heat in the form of a large amount of vapor. This is called bumping. To minimize **bumping**, solutions of liquids that are being heated should be agitated by stirring, swirling, or by the use of the boiling stone. However, never add a boiling stone to an already hot solution, as it may induce a severe bump. The boiling stone provides a nucleation surface for the formation of bubbles, leading to smooth boiling.*

3. The Use of Mixed Solvents in Recrystallization

A mixture of two miscible solvents may be used as the solvent for a recrystallization. In a sense, this procedure amounts to the preparation of your own ideal solvent if no single solvent has been found to be suitable through solubility tests. The only requirement for using mixed solvents is that the solid be at least moderately insoluble in one of the solvents used. The procedure for using mixtures or co-solvents is as follows: The solid is dissolved in a small amount of the hot solvent in which it is very soluble. The hot solvent in which it is insoluble is then added slowly to the boiling solution until a cloudiness appears. More of the first solvent is then added until the boiling solution turns clear again. The solution is then cooled and treated as described in (5) on the following page. This method has the advantage of generally taking less time once the solvents have been selected. Common mixtures that can be used are alcohols and water or chlorinated hydrocarbons and hexane. In these cases, the compounds are usually soluble cold in the alcohols or chlorinated hydrocarbons and only slightly soluble or insoluble in the water or hexane.

4. The Use of Decolorizing Charcoal

The use of decolorizing carbon (actually, activated charcoal) is sometimes successful in removing colored impurities from the product, but if no substantial improvement occurs, the process should not be repeated. The fine carbon particles have a large, active surface which readily attracts and adsorbs many of the resinous, polymeric, colored, and other reactive impurities often found in organic reaction mixtures.

Decolorizing carbon is added to the cold or warm solution just after the solution has been prepared and mixed thoroughly by swirling. The amount to be added should be approximately 2–3 percent of the weight of the product being recrystallized. Any excess will only adsorb part of the product and result in a lower yield.

Since the addition of the activated charcoal may cause the hot mixture to boil over, it is important to cool the mixture somewhat beforehand, and then reheat to boiling after the addition. Activated charcoal can also cause the mixture to bump, possibly throwing the hot contents dangerously out of the flask. This can be minimized by continuous stirring.

The solution must then be filtered to remove the charcoal. If the colored impurity is to be removed from a cold solution, a vacuum filtration may be used to remove the charcoal. If the colored impurity is to be removed from a hot solution, a hot gravity filtration may be necessary (since the compound will recrystallize upon cooling) to remove the charcoal. Decolorization is most convenient when using mixed solvents. The decolorization and filtration can be performed in the "good" solvent (before the second solvent is added), thus avoiding premature recrystallization.

5. Inducing Recrystallization

The Erlenmeyer flask containing the product is now set aside, and the hot filtrate is allowed to *cool slowly and without agitation*. Rapid cooling and agitation are generally undesirable because crystal formation will occur too rapidly, resulting in impurities becoming trapped within the crystal lattice. Once room temperature is reached, the flask can be cooled further in an ice-water bath. The diminished solubility of the product at this lower temperature will produce a larger yield.

If the cooled solute does not crystallize, several techniques can be employed. Further cooling in the ice-water bath may be successful. One can also scratch the inside of the flask with a glass rod. If a small amount of the original solid material was saved, a crystal of this material may be added to "seed" the cooled solution.

Once crystal formation has begun, it is important not to collect the product too early. Otherwise some material may be lost which would have separated from solution with further standing. With this purification technique, patience is a virtue.

The recrystallized solid is usually isolated by vacuum filtration on a Büchner or Hirsch funnel. Suction filtration is usually preferred over gravity filtration because the difference in pressure increases the rate of liquid flow through the filter. This not only saves time, but it reduces evaporation of the solvent in the funnel, which could redeposit impurities back on the product.

The liquid contained in the filter flask after filtration is called the "mother liquor" or filtrate. Often, additional product can be isolated by evaporating some of the solvent from the filtrate and recooling. This additional product is called a "second crop" and should be kept separate from the original product until its degree of purity has been determined by comparing melting points of the first crop and the second crop.

6. Filtration

a. *Filtering a Hot Solution (Gravity Filtration)*

Insoluble impurities are removed by filtering the hot solution before recrystallization begins. If no obvious insoluble impurities are present, this step may be omitted. The most difficult part of this operation is keeping the solution hot during the filtration, so that premature crystallization does not take place during the process. Use of a short-stem or wide-stem funnel minimizes the possible problem of clogging inside the stem from premature crystallization. A heated funnel prevents the cooling of the hot mixture during filtration, which may cause premature crystallization in the filter. You can heat the funnel by placing it at the top of an Erlenmeyer flask containing a small amount of boiling solvent. During the filtration into the flask, the hot vapors will rise up around the funnel and heat it. Fluted filter paper is employed to speed the rate of filtration. The filter paper should be fitted to the funnel so that it does not extend above the rim of the funnel after it has been moistened with solvent.

Before the solution is filtered, a small amount of additional hot solvent should be poured onto the filter to moisten the paper and warm the funnel. This helps to prevent premature crystallization in the funnel stem. If significant crystallization does occur in the filter, it may be possible to wash it through with hot solvent. It is important to remember, however, that too much solvent will prevent maximum crystallization from occurring.

It is always easier to do a hot filtration when mixed solvents are to be used for the recrystallization. In this case, dissolve the compound in a small amount of hot, "good" solvent, and filter the insoluble impurity before continuing with the normal co-solvent routine. This circumvents the problem of premature crystallization.

It should be emphasized that hot filtration should be done with gravity, *not* vacuum filtration, since vacuum filtration both cools and evaporates the solvent at an even faster rate, and this can lead to premature crystallization.

A fluted filter paper may be prepared as shown in the figure below:

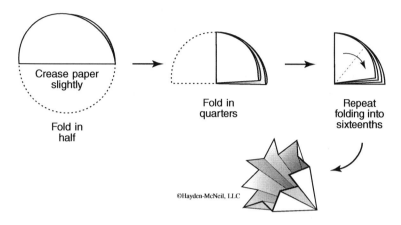

©Hayden-McNeil, LLC

Fluting Filter Paper

b. Filtering the Cold Solution

The apparatus for vacuum filtration (Figure 4-1) consists of a Büchner funnel attached by means of a rubber adapter to a filter flask. Remember that this apparatus is under vacuum, and therefore heavy-walled glass equipment must be used. (Implosions are just as dangerous as explosions.) Only heavy-walled vacuum tubing should be used with this apparatus. The thin-walled tubing that is normally used for condensers will collapse under vacuum and should not be used.

The funnel is fitted with a piece of filter paper of slightly smaller diameter than the filter plate. The paper is wetted with the solvent used (in the case of a two-solvent recrystallization, use the "poor" solvent for wetting the filter paper). After this liquid is filtered through, the paper will cling tightly to the bottom of the funnel so that no small particles of the solid can slip under the paper and reach the filtrate below. With the vacuum fully on, the mixture is *immediately* poured onto the filter. A glass rod may be used to remove all of the crystals from the flask. A *small portion* of fresh, cold solvent is poured into the flask and swirled to remove the last of the crystals. The crystals are then pressed on the filter with a spatula or a clean cork to remove last traces of solution.

The isolated crystals in the funnel are now washed with several *small quantities of fresh, cold* solvent. The purpose of this washing is to remove any impurities that are in the solvent that are on the surface of the crystals. These impurities would remain on the crystals after the solvent evaporated if they weren't rinsed away.

To wash the crystals, first break the vacuum. Then break up the crystalline cake with a spatula, *being careful not to disturb or tear the filter paper.* Next, add enough fresh *cold* solvent to *just cover* the crystals and *carefully* stir the mixture with a spatula to ensure complete rinsing. Then restart the vacuum and remove as much solvent as possible by suction filtration. Remove any additional adhering solvent by pressing with a clean cork. The crystals are then removed from the Büchner funnel and placed on a watch glass or dry filter paper so that they may air-dry.

NOTE: *When removing the funnel from the flask after vacuum filtration, **DO NOT** break the vacuum by turning off the aspirator or vacuum line. Remove the tubing from the flask to break the vacuum, then turn off the vacuum.*

THE EXPERIMENT: SEPARATION AND PURIFICATION OF SOLIDS BY RECRYSTALLIZATION

The main purpose of this experiment is to allow you to practice the technique of recrystallization, one of the best methods for the purification of solids. Associated with recrystallization are the techniques of hot and cold gravity filtration and vacuum filtration. In the first part of this experiment, you will be preparing acetanilide and purifying the reaction product by recrystallization. The preparation of acetanilide involves the treatment of an aromatic amine, aniline, with acetic anhydride to form an amide acetanilide. The overall chemical equation for this reaction is:

Aniline	Acetic anhydride		Acetanilide	Acetic acid

Mechanistically, this is an example of a nucleophilic substitution reaction occurring at an unsaturated carbon.

1. Preparation and Purification of Acetanilide

In a 250 mL Erlenmeyer flask, add 4 mL of aniline. Using the density of aniline, calculate the mass of aniline added. Then add 30 mL of deionized water. While vigorously swirling the reaction flask, add 5 mL of acetic anhydride in small portions. Record observations in your notebook.

The crude acetanilide will now be *recrystallized* (*i.e.*, crystallized again) in the same flask. Add 100 mL of water and a boiling chip, and heat to boiling (swirl frequently) on a hot plate. Continue boiling until *all* of the solid *and* oil have dissolved.

Remove the flask from the heat, and set it aside to cool to room temperature. To complete the recrystallization, chill the flask in an ice bath for 10–15 minutes. Also chill about 15 mL of water (your recrystallizing solvent) while you set up the apparatus for the vacuum filtration (see Figure 4-1). Follow the directions for vacuum filtration—being careful to keep the extra wash with cold solvent to a minimum (2 or 3 mL). Let the solid drain thoroughly over the vacuum for at least 10 minutes and then transfer it to a large piece of filter paper for further air-drying. When the crystals are completely dry, determine the melting point range and weigh the product. Calculate the percent yield, and include this calculation along with the literature value for the melting point in your results.

According to the *Handbook of Chemistry and Physics*, acetanilide melts between 113–114°C and is white. Be sure to discuss in your conclusions such things as: how the literature melting point range compares with that of your product, and what conclusions you can draw from this comparison. When you have completed this experiment, turn in your product in a plastic bag. Label it with your name, grams, percent yield, and melting point range. Staple the bag to your report.

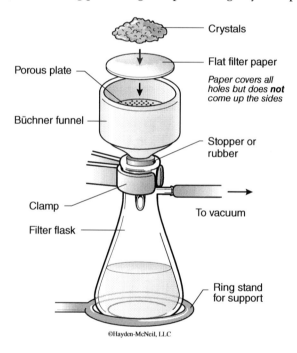

©Hayden-McNeil, LLC

Figure 4-1. *Vacuum Filtration.*

2. *Isolation and Purification of Acetylsalicylic Acid*

In this part of the experiment, you will be separating acetylsalicylic acid, the active ingredient in aspirin tablets, from other compounds commonly found in this consumer product.

Acetylsalicylic acid
(aspirin)

This second purification is the reverse of the first. Here, the desired product, acetylsalicylic acid (aspirin), is soluble in the chosen solvent, ethanol (ethyl alcohol), and the impurities are insoluble. The "impurities" consist of starches and other binders added by the manufacturer to hold the tablet in shape. These materials are of fairly high molecular weight and are known to be relatively insoluble in the common recrystallizing solvents.

In the case of acetylsalicylic acid, there is no good choice of a single solvent in which aspirin is soluble hot and insoluble cold. The compound is partially soluble in cold ethanol, which means that it would be partly lost in a cold filtration. Another possible choice, chloroform, would require a very large volume of the solvent to effect complete solution. This is less desirable than selecting a pair of solvents and conducting a mixed solvent recrystallization. This pair is available in ethanol and water, which are miscible in all proportions, a necessary condition for a mixed solvent recrystallization. Based upon these facts, the following purification procedure was designed for you to try.

Prepare the apparatus for a hot filtration according to the description on page 32, using a short-stemmed funnel and a 125 mL Erlenmeyer flask. Have a fluted filter paper ready. Weigh five aspirin tablets, and put them into the 125 mL Erlenmeyer flask. Place 10 mL of 95% ethanol in the flask, and heat the mixture using a water bath. Swirl the hot mixture until it boils and the tablets disintegrate. You may need to crush the tablets for faster dissolution. At the same time, heat an additional 10 mL of ethanol in a small Erlenmeyer flask, so that it will be hot when you are ready for the filtration.

The solution of acetylsalicylic acid can now be freed of the white residue by hot filtration. First, pour a mL or two of the pure boiling alcohol into the filter paper and the funnel to warm them up. Now, and without delay, pour the mixture of aspirin and impurities into the funnel, and set the filtration apparatus on the hot plate to keep the solution warm. When using a hot plate in this manner, keep the temperature control *low*. When all of the solution has been added to the funnel, pour two or three mL of the pure hot ethanol into the flask and rinse the walls. Add the hot rinse to the funnel. Now, rinse the last traces of solution from the binder by pouring two or three mL of the hot ethanol around the walls of the filter paper.

NOTE: *The volumes of these small rinses are based upon judgment—they need not be measured.*

The impurities are now on the filter paper (which may be discarded), and the pure aspirin is in solution in the flask. Remove the funnel, and while still on the hot plate and with constant stirring, carefully add 25 mL of deionized water to the filtrate in the flask. The water is, in a sense, an anti-solvent; the aspirin is less soluble in the ethanol–water mixture—so much so that it may begin to recrystallize immediately.

NOTE: *Do not assume that one always adds water while performing a recrystallization. Remember, this is a special case, a mixed solvent recrystallization where ethanol and water are a co-solvent pair.*

Remove the flask from the hot plate and allow crystallization to take place for about ten minutes at room temperature. Place the flask in an ice-water bath for about 15 minutes to complete the crystallization. Also, cool about 10 to 15 mL of deionized water to use for rinses. Set up the apparatus for vacuum filtration, and collect the acetylsalicylic acid, rinsing the solid from the flask with *small* portions of the cold water. Wash the product in the funnel with a few mL of the cold water, and allow the product to drain over the vacuum for about 5 minutes. Transfer the product to a large piece of filter paper and let it air dry. When it is completely dry, weigh it and take a melting point.

The amount of active ingredient per tablet (the acetylsalicylic acid) is listed on the aspirin bottle label. Calculate the amount of acetylsalicylic acid in the ten tablets and the weight of the "impurities" (the binders, etc.) that should have been removed.

Calculate the percent recovery, and include this calculation in your results.

Look up the melting point range of acetylsalicylic acid in the *Handbook of Chemistry and Physics* or the *Merck Index*. Be sure to discuss in your conclusions such things as: how does the literature melting point range compare with your product, and what conclusions can you draw from this comparison? When you have completed the experiment, turn in your product in a plastic bag. Label it with your name, grams, percent recovered, and melting point range. Staple the bag to your report.

Questions

1. What is the purpose of a "boiling stone" or chip?

2. When doing a recrystallization, what observations would prompt you to perform a hot filtration?

3. What problems might arise if a hot solution is filtered by vacuum filtration?

4. What is meant when aniline is referred to as the "limiting reagent" in the reaction with acetic anhydride?

5. Under what circumstances would you use mixed solvents in a recrystallization?

6. Why do we keep the volume of the rinses *small* in the recrystallization procedure?

CHAPTER 5

Extraction

INTRODUCTION

Extraction is the separation of a substance from one phase by another phase. You have probably encountered many examples of extraction in daily life, such as extraction of tea from tea leaves or coffee from ground coffee beans. These are examples of **solid–liquid extraction**, where the solid phase is the tea leaves or the coffee grounds and the liquid phase is the solvent, hot water. The process provides us with the ability to isolate many flavorings such as vanilla, almond, and orange extracts, and spearmint and peppermint oils. Certain dyes, drugs, and perfumes are also obtained from natural sources by this method. Extraction, however, is not limited to natural products. Extraction can be the selective transfer of *any* solute or impurity from one phase into another. In the organic laboratory, the most common type of extraction is **liquid–liquid extraction**, where a solute is transferred from one solvent (a liquid phase) into another solvent (another liquid phase). It is a general and very useful method for separating a solute or impurity from other components in a mixture.

THEORY OF EXTRACTION

Extraction is based on the principle of the equilibrium distribution of a substance (the solute) between two immiscible phases, one of which is usually aqueous and the other usually an organic solvent. The aqueous phase may be pure water, or it can be an aqueous solution of a compound that will react with one or more components of the mixture being separated to form a new substance. For example, the use of aqueous $NaHCO_3$ solution to extract organic acids or dilute HCl to extract organic bases from organic solvents is commonly encountered. Extraction is accomplished by shaking a solution of the mixture in a separatory funnel with a second solvent that is immiscible with the solvent in which the mixture is dissolved, but in which the substance to be extracted dissolves more readily. The layer that contains the desired substance can then be isolated by physical separation of the two layers. One extraction will not generally remove all of the substance to be isolated, and usually two or more extractions with lesser amounts of solvent are more effective than one extraction with a large amount of solvent.

When an aqueous solution is mixed with ether, for example, and shaken, the solute distributes itself between the solvents in a ratio proportional to its solubility in each. The term **distribution coefficient** is used to describe the ratio of the concentration of the solute in each solvent (at equilibrium) at a specified temperature. For example, at 20°C, azelaic acid has a solubility in water (C_w) of 0.24 grams per 100 mL of water and in ether (C_e) of 2.70 grams per 100 mL of ether. If we assume that ether and water are totally immiscible, we can calculate the exact value of the distribution coefficient, K_d, using the following relationship:

$$K_d = \frac{g_e \text{ per 100 mL of ether}}{g_w \text{ per 100 mL of water}} = \frac{2.7}{0.24} = 11.25$$

where g_e and g_w are the weights of soluble solute in the given volume of solvent. Because ether actually dissolves in water to the extent of 8 grams per 100 mL of water, this calculation gives only an approximate distribution coefficient.

By knowing the distribution coefficient, one can calculate the amount of material extracted by a given volume of solvent and how much solute remains unextracted. For example, if 0.12 g of azelaic acid in 100 mL of water was extracted with one 100 mL portion of ether, the weight of acid extracted by the ether would be calculated as follows:

$$K_d = \frac{C_e}{C_w} = \frac{g_e/100 \text{ mL}}{(0.12 - g_e) 100 \text{ mL}} = \frac{g_e}{0.12 - g_e} = 11.25$$

Thus g_e is found to be 0.11 g, 92% of the initial sample weight of 0.12 g.

In this case, the solute, azelaic acid, was extracted from water into an inert solvent, ether; *i.e.*, nothing in the solvent reacted with the compound to be extracted, and the extraction depended solely on the difference in the solubility of the azelaic acid in the two solvents. In the experiment you will be performing—which deals with the separation of benzoic acid from *p*-dimethoxybenzene—solvents are employed that react with one of the species to be separated (aqueous hydrochloric acid and aqueous sodium bicarbonate). This is a different situation and will be discussed more fully below.

EXTRACTION TECHNIQUES

Nearly every synthetic reaction which one carries out is followed by a "work-up" procedure to isolate the product of the reaction by the technique of liquid-liquid extraction. The equipment used to carry out an extraction is call a **separatory funnel**. It is important to learn how to use this expensive piece of glassware properly. It is made of relatively thin glass and is easily broken unless handled carefully. The following technique for using the separatory funnel has been found to be satisfactory by most lab workers.

Support the separatory funnel on an iron ring which has been padded (commonly with short sections of rubber tubing split lengthwise and wired to the ring). Make sure that the stopcock is lubricated *unless* it is made of Teflon. Close the stopcock and add to the funnel the liquids to be separated. Insert the stopper, place your finger on it, and invert the funnel as shown in Figure 5-1. Point the barrel away from your face (and that of your neighbor), and open the stopcock to release any pressure that may have developed inside. Close the stopcock and, holding the funnel horizontally, shake the funnel vigorously two or three times. Invert the funnel, and release any pressure via the stopcock as before. Repeat this process until opening the stopcock releases *no* pressure. Now replace the funnel on the iron ring, and *remove the stopper*. Allow the liquids to stand until the layers become clearly defined. Draw the bottom layer into an Erlenmeyer flask (not into a beaker!) of appropriate size, being sure to slow the flow *carefully* as the boundary between the two liquids approaches the stopcock. Stop the flow as soon as the upper layer enters the hole of the stopcock. *Never discard either layer until you are certain which is the proper layer to keep.*

If you are not sure which layer is the aqueous phase and which layer is the organic phase, check the identity of one of the layers by placing a few drops of the layer into a test tube containing water. If the layer is aqueous, this mixture should be homogeneous. If the layer is organic, two layers will be formed. Most organic materials are less dense than water. The halogenated hydrocarbons are one exception, being more dense than water.

Acidic or basic organic compounds are often encountered among the starting materials or products of organic syntheses. The solubility properties of these organic acids and bases and their salts allow us to separate these materials from other, neutral organic molecules. Organic amines of five or fewer carbon atoms, RNH_2, can be extracted by simply washing the organic phase with water. If the other products are neutral, and the amine is not water soluble, extraction with dilute aqueous mineral acid will remove the amine as its water-soluble ammonium salt, $RNH_3^{\oplus}X^{\ominus}$. Carboxylic acids, RCOOH, where R has five or more carbon atoms, are insoluble in water but can be conveniently separated by extraction with dilute aqueous base, usually carbonate or bicarbonate. Many times, advantage can be taken of specific chemical properties to purify complex reaction mixtures by planning a series of extractions.

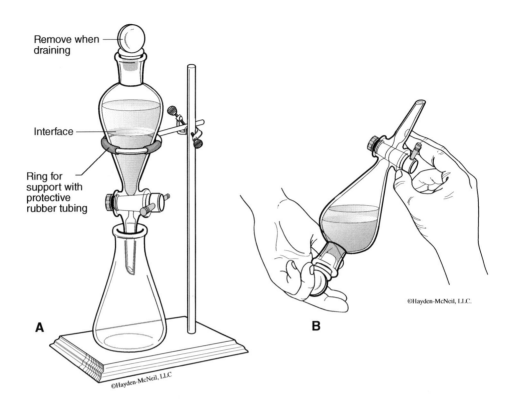

©Hayden-McNeil, LLC.

©Hayden-McNeil, LLC

A

B

Figure 5-1. *(a) Separation of Two Immiscible Liquids with a Separatory Funnel.*
(b) Method of Holding a Separatory Funnel for Washing or
Extracting One Liquid with Another.

Here is an example of how knowledge of acid–base chemistry and extraction can be used for effective separation:

From our general chemistry background in acid–base chemistry, recall that pK_a, ($-\log K_a$), is a measure of acid strength, *i.e.*, stronger acids have higher K_a values and hence, lower pK_a values. Sodium carbonate will convert acids stronger than pK_a of 7 ($K_a = 10^{-7}$) to their water-soluble salts, while a stronger base such as sodium hydroxide will react with acids stronger than pK_a 14 ($K_a = 10^{-14}$) to form water-soluble salts. Consider a mixture containing naphthalene, a neutral substance, benzoic acid, a water-insoluble solid with a pK_a of about 4, and phenol, a partially water-soluble aromatic alcohol with a pK_a of about 10. All are soluble in ether. It is obvious that the hydroxide ion will react with both the benzoic acid and the phenol. This is what we propose to do. First, we dissolve the sample in ether. Then, we extract with aqueous sodium carbonate solution and take out the benzoic acid as its sodium salt. Then we extract the ether solution with aqueous sodium hydroxide and remove the phenol as its sodium salt (sodium phenoxide). Now the ether solution contains only naphthalene. Evaporation of the ether will give us the naphthalene, which we can recrystallize if necessary. The two aqueous solutions (one containing sodium benzoate and the other containing sodium phenoxide) can now be treated with strong mineral acid. (Remember that a strong acid will protonate the salt of a weak acid and regenerate the weak acid.) For example, treatment with aqueous hydrochloric acid results in the protonation of the benzoate anion, giving back benzoic acid, which is water-insoluble and should crystallize. Since the benzoic acid is back in its water-insoluble form, it is also in its ether-soluble form and can either be filtered or extracted into ether to separate it from the aqueous medium. The general equation for this last reaction is:

The same treatment can be applied to the sodium phenoxide solution, but phenol will be obtained as a partially water-soluble oil which must be isolated from the aqueous phase by extraction with ether.

From this example you can see that extraction can play a very important role in separation. In organic chemistry, fractional distillation, extraction, and chromatography are the most important techniques for the separation of complex mixtures into individual components.

An **emulsion** is a dispersion of very fine droplets of one immiscible liquid in another, and can be very troublesome if it occurs during an attempted extraction. In order to avoid emulsions in cases where the tendency for them to form is known in advance, the separatory funnel should be carefully swirled and not vigorously shaken. If an emulsion does form, addition of ionic salts such as sodium chloride or potassium sulfate will sometimes help by reducing the surface tension of the water droplets. When all else fails, ask your instructor for help in dealing with an emulsion.

The technique of extraction requires the student to think and plan. Wherever possible, choose the solvents so that the extracting medium is the lower layer and the medium to be extracted is the upper layer. For example, if you are going to attempt to extract a reaction mixture with an aqueous phase, choose to dissolve the mixture in ether. Ether is less dense than water, allowing the aqueous phase to be drawn off after each successive addition, with the organic phase remaining in the separatory funnel. Conversely, if your mixture is primarily in an aqueous phase and you want to extract the organic components, choose methylene chloride, CH_2Cl_2, as your solvent. This chlorinated hydrocarbon is denser than water, and the mixture can be repeatedly extracted with fresh portions of CH_2Cl_2 which are drawn off, leaving the mixture in the separatory funnel until extraction is complete. Such thinking and planning can save time and effort.

In summary, several desirable solvent properties for extraction are listed below:

1. The extraction solvent should be insoluble or only slightly soluble in the solvent from which the desired compounds are being extracted.

   Therefore, ethyl alcohol, which is soluble with water in all proportions, would not be a suitable solvent for extracting from an aqueous solution.

2. The extraction solvent should have a favorable distribution coefficient for the substance being extracted and an unfavorable distribution coefficient for any other components in the mixture. Otherwise, a selective transfer of just the substance being extracted will not occur. In addition, the solvent may not dissolve much of the substance, resulting in a large volume, and perhaps many extractions will be necessary for a complete transfer.

3. The extraction solvent should be easily removed from the extracted substance after the extraction procedure. Since the removal is often carried out by distillation, the solvent should have a reasonably low boiling point.

4. The extraction solvent should be chemically inert to the extracted substance, to other components in the mixture, as well as to the solvent of the solution being extracted. The exception here, of course, is the case of solvents such as aqueous acid or base as described above.

5. The extraction solvent should be reasonably safe to work with and relatively inexpensive.

   Ethyl ether is the organic solvent most frequently used in liquid–liquid extractions. It has the advantages of relative inertness, high solvent power for most organic compounds, and a low boiling point (which makes it easy to remove). Its disadvantages include its high flammability and solvent loss due to its high volatility.

   Methylene chloride (dichloromethane) is also frequently used. It has the advantages of relative inertness, high solvent power for most organic compounds, low flammability, and a low boiling point, which makes it easy to remove. Its disadvantages include its toxicity and solvent loss due to its high volatility.

   Other extraction solvents are: hexane (or ligroin), pentane (or petroleum ether), ethyl acetate, and toluene. Benzene and chloroform have now been removed from this list because of their carcinogenic nature.

DRYING AGENTS

Small amounts of moisture can sharply inhibit the crystallization of many solids. In addition, many liquids when distilled in the presence of water react chemically with water (*i.e.*, are hydrolyzed) or they distill (or steam distill) with the water at temperatures far removed from their true boiling points. For these reasons, the usual final step in an extraction procedure prior to the isolation of a solid, or the distillation of a liquid, is the removal of residual water through some drying process. This is usually accomplished while the organic compound is still dissolved in the organic solvent used in the extraction.

A good chemical drying agent (1) must be chemically compatible with the substance to be dried, (2) should have a high intensity (remove water completely or nearly so), (3) should have a high capacity (remove a large amount of water per unit weight of desiccant), (4) should act rapidly, and (5) should be removed easily from the dried substances.

Chemical drying agents may be divided broadly into two classes: (1) those which react chemically with water by an irreversible process giving rise to a new, water-free compound; and (2) those that combine reversibly with water, either by hydrate formation or by adsorption.

Class 1	Class 2
Sodium metal	Sodium sulfate, anhydrous
Calcium hydride	Magnesium sulfate, anhydrous
Calcium oxide	Calcium chloride, anhydrous
Phosphoric anhydride	Calcium sulfate, anhydrous
	Potassium carbonate, anhydrous
	Sodium or potassium hydroxide
	Molecular sieves
	Silica gel

Most drying of organic substances in the beginning laboratory is carried out by using the anhydrous salts of the second class. The relative merits of a few of the more common drying agents are discussed here.

Sodium Sulfate, a neutral salt, is cheap and has a high capacity, but it is slow and of low intensity. Its usual use is for the removal of moderate amounts of water from ether solutions. It is not good with benzene, toluene, or chloroform. When this salt is used for drying, it tends to form granular masses at the bottom of the flask. The dried solution can be easily decanted, thus avoiding a filtration step.

Magnesium Sulfate, an acidic salt, is an excellent all-purpose desiccant with good capacity and good intensity. It is cheap and fairly rapid, but it has been known to catalyze some transformations which require only trace amounts of acid. This salt is a fine powder and must be removed by filtration from the dried solution. Take care that you use enough of this drying agent to remove all of the water. If the salt takes on the appearance of an oily second layer in the bottom of the flask, you need to add more of the anhydrous powder.

Calcium Chloride, in the form of pellets, is an inexpensive drying agent of high capacity which acts rapidly. Caution must be exercised in the use of this salt, as it is somewhat reactive toward amines and alcohols.

Calcium Sulfate is extremely rapid and efficient but has low capacity. It is often used after a primary desiccant such as sodium sulfate. It is found under the tradename **Drierite**. This salt is often found as large chunks but is sometimes powdery, and must usually be filtered for removal. Be careful not to use the Drierite which is tinted blue since the dye is soluble in some organic solvents.

DRYING TECHNIQUES

The actual drying technique is quite simple. The solution of the compound in the organic solvent is placed in an Erlenmeyer flask, and the drying agent is added to it. A rough rule of thumb is to use a heaping teaspoon for each 100 mL of solution to be dried. With magnesium and calcium sulfate, 20–30 minutes of exposure with occasional swirling is sufficient to remove moisture. Sodium sulfate should really be left overnight. When drying is judged to be complete, the drying agent is usually removed by gravity filtration through fluted filter paper. With a coarse grade of calcium sulfate or calcium chloride, glass wool may be sufficient to remove the solid completely. If the particles of drying agent are sufficiently large, the dried solution can be decanted rather than filtered to remove the drying agent. This can improve yield and is the method of choice where applicable. If the drying agent must be removed by filtration, remember to rinse the solid with a few milliliters of the solvent and to rinse the flask and filter paper as well. Since the goal is to recover the highest possible yield, a small volume of additional solvent makes this possible. Remember, you are going to evaporate the solvent; therefore, the quantity of solvent is not critical.

SOLVENT REMOVAL

After a reaction has been performed and the products have been partially separated through extraction (often referred to as the "work-up"), the organic chemist is faced with the removal of the solvent in order to obtain the crude product. If the product is a liquid, the dried extracts can be distilled using a conventional distillation apparatus.

Atmospheric distillation of the solvent is not advisable where solids are to be isolated, as they may be accidentally decomposed or heated excessively while still impure. Commercial rotary-style evaporators are useful for solvent removal at reduced pressure and temperature and are very efficient. They are, however, expensive pieces of equipment.

If the solvents to be evaporated are low boiling, such as ether, pentane, or methylene chloride, they may be evaporated in a good fume hood from an Erlenmeyer flask by placing them in a water bath or on a steam bath. If a source of *clean, dry* air or inert gas (nitrogen or argon) under low to moderate pressure is available, a slow stream of gas passing across the surface of the solution being evaporated will also hasten evaporation. Care should be taken to avoid excessive splashing by keeping the stream of gas slow. The gas can be introduced by using a short length of glass tubing bent at a right angle attached to the gas outlet by a length of rubber tubing.

> **NOTE: Do not** use the natural gas outlet for this purpose.

> **REMEMBER:** It is not good practice to evaporate any solvent into the laboratory airspace shared by all.

THE EXPERIMENT

Separation and Purification of Solids
Separation of *p*-Dimethoxybenzene and Benzoic Acid by Extraction

This section describes the procedure for separating a neutral ether, *p*-dimethoxybenzene (also called hydroquinone dimethyl ether), from an acidic compound, benzoic acid. Two types of drying agents and two different but common extraction solvents will be used for the purpose of gaining experience with the relative advantages and disadvantages of each.

p–Dimethoxybenzene
(*hydroquinone dimethyl ether*)

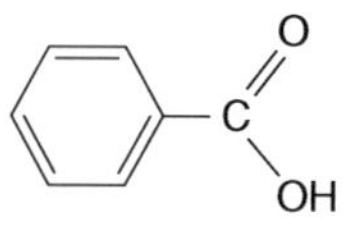

Benzoic acid

EXTRACTION TECHNIQUE

Separation of Benzoic Acid and Dimethoxybenzene

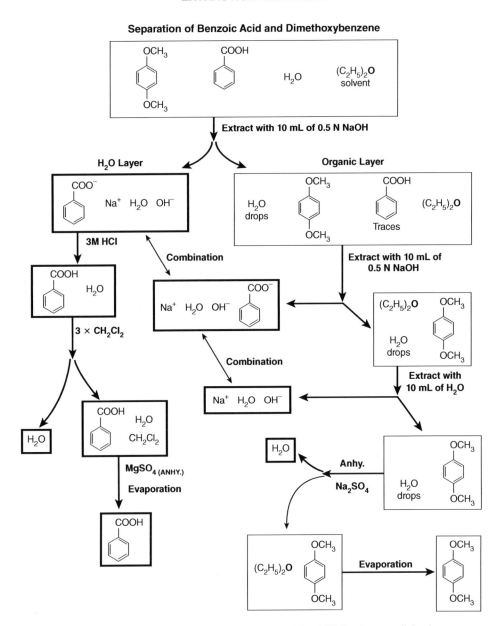

Figure 5-2. *Flowchart Describing Exactly What Will Be Accomplished in This Procedure of Separation by Extraction.*

Procedure

Weigh out approximately one gram of the dimethoxybenzene/benzoic acid mixture into a small Erlenmeyer flask. Obtain about 45 mL of diethyl ether (usually referred to as just ether), and cool the ether in an ice bath for a few minutes. Use a small amount of the cooled ether to dissolve the mixture, and transfer the resulting solution to a separatory funnel. Continue rinsing the small Erlenmeyer flask using the rest of the cooled ether, combining all of the ether rinses in the separatory funnel. Add about 10 mL of *cooled* 0.5 N sodium hydroxide solution to the separatory funnel, and shake the mixture in the proper manner. The benzoic acid will react with the base and form the water-soluble benzoate anion ($C_6H_5COO^\ominus$).

Draw off the aqueous phase (on the bottom because water is denser than ether) into a 125 mL Erlenmeyer flask, and add a second, fresh 10 mL portion of chilled sodium hydroxide solution to the ether solution in the separatory funnel. Shake again to remove any traces of benzoic acid which might remain in the ether. Shake well as before, draw off the aqueous phase, and combine it with the first portion. This is called **successive extraction** and when performing such, you should always combine the like fractions.

The neutral dimethoxybenzene now remains in the ether layer, and the benzoic acid has been transferred to the aqueous phase. To assure that all traces of the base (NaOH) are gone, extract the ether layer with 10 mL of cooled, deionized water, and add this to the other aqueous extracts.

The ether layer is *poured from the top* into a clean, dry, labeled, 250 mL Erlenmeyer flask.

> **NOTE:** *Although it might seem more sensible to drain the ether through the stopcock, water trapped in the stopcock bore and clinging to the walls of the funnel will also drain out, requiring the use of larger amounts of drying agent later.*

Dry the ether layer by adding *anhydrous* sodium sulfate to the solution and swirling the mixture until some loose, unclumped crystals remain. Stopper the flask and set it aside.

The aqueous phase should now be acidified in order to regenerate the benzoic acid. After washing the separatory funnel well with water, pour the aqueous phase back into the separatory funnel, and add about 5 mL of cooled 3 M hydrochloric acid. Check the pH of the solution with pH paper after the addition to be sure that it is acidic; if it is not, add more acid—a few drops at a time—until the test paper indicates the solution is acidic. A white precipitate of benzoic acid, which is insoluble in water, should have formed at this point.

The benzoic acid will now be extracted into a different solvent, methylene chloride. Successively extract the benzoic acid with three 10 mL portions of methylene chloride. *Remember what successive means!* This does *not* mean that you measure out 10 mL of solvent three times and put all three portions in at once! Also, remember which layer is the methylene chloride layer! When you have completed the three extractions, combine the three methylene chloride extracts in a 250 mL Erlenmeyer flask. Dry the extracts with anhydrous magnesium sulfate using the same procedure that you used above for the sodium sulfate drying of the ether. Stopper and label the flask, and set it aside to dry.

You now have: (1) two organic phases containing the separated compounds (*p*-dimethoxybenzene in ether and benzoic acid in methylene chloride) and (2) the aqueous phase (which should still be in the separatory funnel). Set the aqueous phase aside temporarily. Remember, it is recommended that you not throw anything away until you are sure that you have your products in hand.

Decant or filter the two organic solutions into two pre-weighed 50 mL Erlenmeyer flasks. Evaporate the solvent from both flasks using a hot water bath in the hood. Swirl the flasks from time to time to aid in the evaporation. When all of the solvent appears to have evaporated from the two flasks, cool them in ice, dry the outside of the flasks, and reweigh them to obtain the weight of each product.

Scrape out a bit of each solid, and take the melting point of each product. Compare your melting points with the literature values. Calculate the percent *total* recovery of the two compounds (*i.e.*, the sum of the two compounds, not the percentage of each) that were in the original mixture. Hand in the products, in labeled plastic bags.

Questions

1. Why would ethyl alcohol not be a good solvent to use with water in an extraction?

2. How does the extraction procedure differ when the organic phase is (a) less dense than water and (b) more dense than water? What differences did you observe between the two drying agents that you used in today's extraction procedures?

3. What is the purpose of venting the separatory funnel by occasionally opening the stopcock during the shaking process? Why is there a buildup of pressure even when no gas is being produced by a chemical reaction?

4. What is the biggest safety hazard in this experiment?

5. Describe a procedure that might be used to separate *p*-dichlorobenzene (a neutral compound) from *p*-chloroaniline (a basic compound) by extraction.

6. Why is it necessary to remove the stopper from the separatory funnel when the liquid is being drained from it through the stopcock?

CHAPTER 6

Chromatography

In 1903, a Russian botanist, Michael Tswett, extracted a mixture of pigments from green leaves and then washed the mixture with petroleum ether through a glass tube packed with powdered calcium carbonate. As the mixture passed down the chalk-filled tube, the pigments became separated, forming a number of distinctly colored zones. The name **chromatography**, meaning the graphing of colors, was given by Tswett to this separation technique.

The word "chromatography" is still used today, even though the technique is more commonly used with colorless compounds. It is a widely employed analytical tool that is often at the forefront of new discoveries in chemistry, biology, medicine, pharmacy, clinical chemistry, forensic science, and the environmental sciences. In its various forms, the method has proven to be a tremendous breakthrough for modern chemistry, since it allows complex mixtures to be readily separated, even when only very small quantities of materials are used. As such, chromatography has developed into the premier technique for separation and analysis.

Chromatography is essentially a physical method of separation.

The most common forms of chromatography involve two phases, one mobile and one stationary. The mobile or moving phase is usually a liquid or a gas, and the stationary phase may be a solid or a liquid which is adsorbed on the surface of a solid. A sample of the mixture is inserted at or near the point where contact is first made between the two phases. The components of the sample then migrate. The theory of migration is based on the repeated passage of molecules back and forth between the two phases. Any one molecule will spend time, t_s, adsorbed on the stationary phase and time, t_m, dissolved in the mobile phase. During time t_m, the molecule moves at the velocity of the mobile gas or liquid; during time t_s, it is not moving at all. Molecules are carried along at different rates depending on their relative affinity for the two phases. A measure of this affinity is the distribution ratio, K, which is defined simply as:

$$K = \frac{t_s}{t_m}$$

Chromatography, then, involves a complex equilibrium of solute molecules with the two phases, and the success of the separation can be influenced by many variables. These variables are discussed as needed under the specific types of chromatographic separation.

The common types of chromatographic systems are:

1. Partition between a solid and a liquid [thin layer chromatography (TLC), column chromatography, and high performance liquid chromatography (HPLC)]

2. Partition between a liquid and a gas [gas–liquid chromatography (GC)]

3. Ion exchange

For organic chemists, the first two types are by far the most important techniques. The first is known as adsorption chromatography, and it encompasses two of the general chromatographic techniques we will use, **thin layer chromatography** and **column chromatography**. The second type is gas–liquid phase chromatography (GLPC, or simply GC), commonly known as **gas chromatography**.

In general, one chooses from among these chromatographic techniques on the basis of the volatility of the mixture to be separated. Nonvolatile solids and liquids may be separated by adsorption chromatography, while volatile solids, liquids, and gases may be separated by gas chromatography. Gas chromatography and thin layer chromatography are the techniques of choice for analytical (*i.e.*, small-scale) studies, while any of the methods may be configured for preparative (*i.e.*, large-scale) separations.

THIN LAYER CHROMATOGRAPHY (TLC)

In thin layer chromatography (TLC) molecules have a certain affinity or attraction to a stationary phase (usually silica or alumina) which has been coated onto the surface of a glass or plastic plate, and a different affinity for the solvent (the mobile phase) which is moving up the plate by capillary action.

The overall process of TLC consists of applying a small droplet of a dilute solution containing the mixture to be separated near one end of the plate, developing the chromatogram with solvent, then observing the results by a visualization technique.

The actual chromatographic separation is caused by the interaction of the sample molecules and the solvent molecules with the surface of the adsorbent. The adsorbent is a solid with a large surface area exposing a large number of polar sites that can reversibly bind (adsorb) small concentrations of added substances by electrostatic forces of attraction. As fresh solvent moves up the plate by capillary action, the adsorbed material comes into equilibrium with the solvent, and the sample molecules compete for the adsorbent with the solvent which is displacing the sample reversibly and continuously in the direction of travel of the solvent "front." This process can be thought of as a three-way competition between the sample, the solvent, and the adsorbent, as expressed in the following equilibria:

sample–adsorbent ⇌ solvent–adsorbent ⇌ sample–solvent

As the solvent passes through fresh adsorbent, the material is constantly redeposited, and by this process of successive desorption and adsorption, the material moves up the plate.

When a sample has been deposited on the adsorbent in the form of a **spot**, the coated plate is placed in a jar or beaker containing a small amount of some solvent or solvent mixture, such that the lower end of the plate dips 1–2 mm below the surface of the solvent. With the jar covered, the solvent is drawn vertically up the coated surface by capillary action and travels past the point at which the sample was applied. The components in the sample move with the solvent up the coated surface at *different rates* depending on a number of factors.

The rate of elution of the sample components will depend in part on the nature of the components. Polar or polarizable compounds such as alcohols (ROH), carboxylic acids (RCOOH), and amides (RCONH$_2$) are adsorbed more strongly and are eluted less readily than less polar compounds such as halogen compounds (RCl), aldehydes and ketones (RCHO and R$_2$CO), ethers (ROR'), and hydrocarbons (RH).

The solvent used to elute the sample will also affect the rate of elution. The more polar the solvent, the more rapidly the components will move, because more polar solvents offer more competition for active adsorbent sites. It follows, therefore, that the choices of solvent will be dictated by the natures of the components to be separated, with polar solvents being used for strongly adsorbed components and nonpolar solvents for weakly adsorbed components.

The activity of the solid adsorbent will also have an effect on the rate at which the components are eluted. In the case of silica gel, which is commonly used, its activity (or affinity for the sample components) will be greatly affected by its water content. The more water in the coating, the lower will be its activity. In preparing a coating, a slurry of the gel in water is spread evenly over a glass or flexible plastic plate, and the coating is then activated by drying the coated plate in an oven for 30–60 minutes at about 100–120°C.

The **ratio** of the distance that a substance has moved to the distance traversed by the solvent is called the **R$_f$ value** for the compound. R$_f$ values can aid in the identification of substances when measurements are made under the same conditions; this usually means carrying out comparative chromatograms at the same time. Various features of a TLC plate are shown in the following diagram:

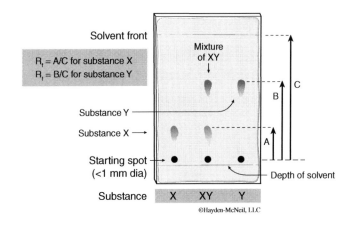

Figure 6-1. *Features of a TLC Plate.*

For a good separation of components in the mixture being analyzed, the eluting solvent should be polar enough so that the components move from the origin, but not so polar that they move with the solvent front.

If a single solvent does not give good separation of components, a solvent mixture may work better. Solvent mixtures may have two or three components, such as 6:1 chloroform-methanol or 90:5:5 benzene-ethyl acetate-acetic acid.

Solvents Listed in Approximate Order of Polarity

Least Polar

Cyclohexane

Petroleum ether

Pentane

Carbon tetrachloride

Benzene

Toluene

Chloroform

Ethyl ether

Ethyl acetate

Ethanol

Acetone

Acetic acid

Methanol

Water

Most Polar

There are two common techniques used to visualize spots on a TLC plate. First, looking at the slide under an ultraviolet light will show any compounds that absorb ultraviolet light. This would be the case for compounds containing benzene rings or conjugated systems. Next, placing the plate in an iodine chamber allows iodine to collect on the spots by a weak electronic interaction. This will cause the spots to take on a dark brown color and therefore become visible. If the slide is removed from the chamber, the iodine will sublime off over the course of a few minutes.

Thin Layer Chromatography Techniques

For very precise separations, plates which are up to eight inches long are utilized. The coating can be a thin one, or if large amounts of material are to be separated and their recovery attempted, the coating can be made thicker. The use of **thick layer chromatography** to isolate small amounts of a pure substance from a complex mixture is a common tool in research laboratories investigating the structure and reactivity of natural products.

The TLC plates used in the student laboratory are commercially prepared plates using a flexible plastic support instead of glass.

Applying a Spot to a TLC Plate

Dip a **spotter**, which is made from a length of capillary tubing, into a solution of the sample to be analyzed. The solution will be drawn into the tubing by capillary action. Now touch the end of the tubing against a thin layer plate at a point about 0.5 cm from one end. The solution will drain onto the coating. Allow the solvent to evaporate for 5–10 seconds, then make a second application in the same manner *on top of the same spot*. Depending upon the concentration of the solution being examined, you may wish to spot several times to build up enough of a concentration of the material to be analyzed. Now apply a second sample at a different place but in line with the first spot. In this manner, a plate may be spotted with several different samples, depending upon the width of the plate. Where an identification of a substance is to be made, allow space for spotting with a solution of the reference compound so that it can be developed simultaneously and side by side with the unknown.

With a fine pencil, draw a straight line across the coating about 3–5 mm from the upper edge of the plate. Take care not to disturb the coating between this line and the lower edge of the plate. The plate is now ready to be developed.

Prepare a developing chamber using a beaker that is covered with a watch glass, and line the chamber with a strip of filter paper. Cut the filter paper so as to leave a space for viewing the plate (see Figure 6-2). Place a small amount (5 mL or less) of solvent on the bottom of the covered beaker. Carefully lower the slide into the beaker such that the bottom of the slide rests squarely in the center of the lined chamber. The chromatogram will be ruined if the solvent covers the point of application of the sample. Place the cover in position and observe the passage of the solvent up the surface of the plate. When the solvent reaches the line at the top of the plate, remove the plate from the bottle and allow the solvent to evaporate (1–2 minutes). Do not allow the plate to remain in the developing chamber after the solvent has reached the top line.

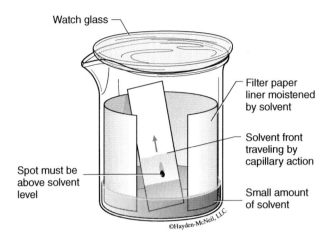

Watch glass

Filter paper liner moistened by solvent

Solvent front traveling by capillary action

Spot must be above solvent level

Small amount of solvent

©Hayden-McNeil, LLC

Figure 6-2. *Apparatus for Development of a TLC Plate.*

If the compounds are colored, the spots are very easy to identify. Locating spots when the components are colorless may be done in a number of ways. The most convenient methods involve:

1. irradiation with ultraviolet light.

2. reversible association with iodine.

3. spraying with a reagent which colors the spot (*e.g.*, H_2SO_4, ninhydrin, etc.).

With methods 2 and 3, the spots are visible. When the spots are observed through the use of ultraviolet light (method 1), you must use a sharp-pointed pencil to circle the spot while it is illuminated so that its position can be measured later.

As soon as the plates are dry and you have located and marked the spots, use a ruler to measure the distance from the point of application (start) to the line drawn across the top of the plate. Then measure the distance traveled by each spot, and calculate an R_f value for each compound. See Figure 6-1.

Note that:

$$\text{for spot X, } R_f = \frac{A\,(\text{Distance traveled by the component})}{C\,(\text{Distance traveled by the solvent front})}$$

$$\text{for spot Y, } R_f = \frac{B\,(\text{Distance traveled by the component})}{C\,(\text{Distance traveled by the solvent front})}$$

It is of particular importance to note here that R_f values are not reproducible with great accuracy due to the wide variety of variables which affect TLC. It is recommended that you *always* spot a known; *i.e.*, a reference sample of the compound alongside any unknown which has to be tentatively identified.

COLUMN CHROMATOGRAPHY

The theory behind the separation of mixtures by column chromatography is identical to that for thin layer chromatography. In column chromatography, however, the solid adsorbent is contained in a vertical tube, and the sample is applied to the top of the column in a small volume of solvent. Solvent is allowed to flow through the adsorbent in the column by gravity flow.

In contrast to thin layer chromatography, rather than *developing* a chromatographic plate until the solvent front reaches the end of the plate, the mobile phase is passed through a column until the components of interest *elute from* (wash off) the column. In column chromatography, the sample components pass through the stationary phase as bands rather than spots as previously seen with TLC. The most strongly adsorbed compounds are held at the top, and the ones having less affinity for the adsorbent appear at lower levels.

As in the case of thin layer chromatography, the chromatographic separation is caused by the interaction of the sample molecules and the solvent molecules with the surface of the adsorbent. The adsorbent solid has a large surface area exposing a large number of polar sites that can reversibly bind (adsorb) small concentrations of added substances by electrostatic forces of attraction. As fresh solvent is passed through the column, the adsorbed material at the top of the column comes into equilibrium with the solvent, and the sample molecules compete for the adsorbent with the solvent which is displacing the sample reversibly and continuously in the direction of travel of the solvent "front."

As the solvent passes through fresh adsorbent, the material is redeposited, and by this process of successive desorption and adsorption, the material passes down the column.

As a result of this process, the individual components of the mixture pass down the column in bands that travel at rates proportional to the degree of adsorption.

Choice of the stationary phase (adsorbent) and mobile phase (solvent) is governed by the same factors discussed in the TLC experiment. The solvent used to develop the column is the least polar solvent that permits movement of material on the column at a practical rate. The preferred solvent is often determined by first subjecting the mixture to thin layer chromatography (TLC).

Typical practice is to start with a fairly nonpolar solvent which will elute poorly adsorbed, nonpolar components and switch to successively more polar solvents (or mixtures of solvents) to remove the more strongly adsorbed, polar components. Choice of solvent must be done carefully, for one that is too polar will wash the mixture off the column without allowing separation, and one that is not polar enough will not move the compounds down the column.

The following series of solvents listed in order of increasing eluting power offers a guideline for selection of a solvent.

**Eluting Power of Solvents
(Increasing Order) Against Alumina**

Least Eluting Power

Hexane
Cyclohexane
Carbon tetrachloride
Trichloroethylene
Toluene
Dichloromethane
Chloroform
Diethyl ether
Ethyl acetate
Acetone
1,2-Dichloroethane
Ethanol
Methanol
Water
Pyridine
Organic Acids

Most Eluting Power

The composition of the eluting solvent may be changed over a narrow range of polarity by slowly increasing the percentage of the next solvent. For example, 5% diethyl ether in chloroform, followed by 10% ether in chloroform, then 15% ether, etc.

Two of the main advantages of column chromatography are that it requires simple apparatus, and the purification obtained is very high. Unfortunately, it also has its drawbacks. It can be fairly time consuming, the choice of adsorbent and solvent must be empirically determined by a series of trial experiments, and it is not convenient if large quantities of material are to be purified. Thus, if one of the components of the mixture can be partially recovered by recrystallization, it is wise to do this before proceeding to chromatography. However, if only small quantities are used, chromatography is by far the better procedure.

Chromatography, like most analytical techniques, has become highly instrumentalized in the past few years. Column chromatography in particular has changed dramatically from the type just described. HPLC, which stands for high performance liquid chromatography, employs the same principles of separation as open column chromatography, but the particles of the stationary phase are only three to ten *micro*meters in diameter, and it is packed into small diameter (1–5 mm) stainless steel tubing. The density of the packing is such that there is no gravity flow of solvent through the column, so the mobile phase must be forced through the column under high pressure (as high as several thousand psi). The small diameter stationary phase gives an extremely high surface area for contact between the mobile phase and the solutes, and therefore the exchange of solute between the two phases occurs many more times per unit length of column. This then yields highly efficient separations. It is even possible under certain conditions to resolve pairs of optically active compounds with a column only a few centimeters in length! A detailed study of HPLC is beyond the scope of this course, but will be found in more advanced analytical texts.

The Preparation of a Column

Obtain a chromatography column suitable for the amount of adsorbent required in the experiment, and secure it to a ring stand with a clamp. Close the stopcock, and fill the column 2/3 full of hexane or petroleum ether (unless the experiment calls for another solvent to be used). Do not fill to the very top; there must be room for a powder funnel to fit into the top of the column without the tip of the funnel coming in contact with the liquid. With the help of a long glass rod, insert a small plug of glass wool or cotton into the top of the column, and push it down to the bottom. This serves to hold the column and prevent any solid from getting into the stopcock or drip tip.

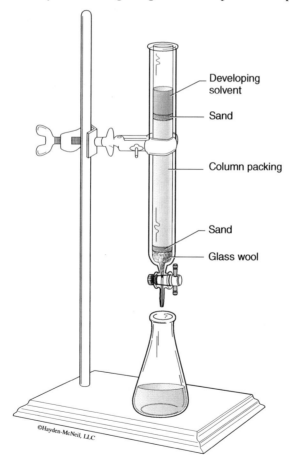

Figure 6-3. Apparatus for Column Chromatography.

Pour in 1/4–1/2 inch of clean sand. Weigh out the amount of adsorbent, and pour it slowly into the powder funnel so that it falls slowly through the solvent in the column and settles at the bottom. The level of the liquid in the column will rise because of the addition of the solid material and must be watched and continuously lowered to prevent the tip of the funnel from becoming wet.

While the adsorbent is settling to the bottom, it is helpful to tap the side of the column gently with the fingers, a cork ring, or a piece of thick-walled tubing to help release trapped air bubbles and to settle the bed uniformly. After all the adsorbent has been introduced and has settled, add an additional 1/4 inch of sand to the top of the bed. The solvent should now be run down to just above the top of the bed.

Specific instructions as to exactly how to apply the mixture to the column and carry out the elution itself is discussed in the procedure section of the column chromatography experiment.

GAS CHROMATOGRAPHY

Vapor phase chromatography (more commonly called gas chromatography) was introduced in 1952 by the British chemist, A.J.P. Martin, and its rapid application to all branches of chemistry and to many other sciences is an indication of the usefulness of the method.

Gas chromatography is similar in principle to thin layer and column chromatography, but differs in the following ways:

1. Instead of the stationary phase on the column being a solid adsorbent such as silica gel or alumina, a nonvolatile liquid or solid such as silicone oil, hydrocarbon grease, or polyethylene glycol is used as a coating on an inert, powdered support material such as crushed firebrick or diatomaceous earth.

2. The mobile phase, instead of being a liquid, is an inert gas, such as helium or nitrogen.

3. The separation of the components in the mixture depends on how strongly these compounds are adsorbed on the stationary phase and on their relative vapor pressures, which will determine their solubility in the moving gas phase.

4. The nature of the carrier gas does not affect the solubility and the resulting movement of the components in the mixture. Therefore, the polarity or nonpolarity of the mobile phase does not affect the separation.

5. The temperature of the column can be changed and plays an important role, since column temperature will directly influence the vapor pressures of the mixture components.

The principal limitation of GC is that the compounds under study must have some vapor pressure. A vapor pressure less than 1 mm is sufficient, and temperatures up to 300°C may be employed if the compounds are stable at such temperatures; therefore, a minimum volatility is required. Anything that may be distilled, even at a pressure as low as 0.01 mm, may be gas chromatographed, and GC is a vastly more effective method of separation than is distillation. Compounds boiling two degrees apart, scarcely separable by distillation with the best equipment, may be separated by GC so easily that they will come out of the column a minute or more apart. Indeed, compounds with identical boiling points are separable by GC. Gas chromatography may be applied to very small amounts: 1 mg is a normal sample size used for analysis, and quantities of 1 microgram (1 μg, 0.001 mg) or less can be utilized. Separation of large quantities (more than about 50 mg) by GC can also be accomplished, but such "preparative" separations necessitate the use of large diameter columns.

In the most commonly used type of gas phase chromatography, the mixture to be analyzed is passed through a heated column (usually of 1/4" O.D.) made of glass, aluminum, or stainless steel tubing, packed with an inert support phase that has been impregnated with a stationary phase. The carrier gas is usually helium or nitrogen. In addition to proper selection of a stationary phase, other important considerations affecting overall separation are column length, column diameter, column temperature, flow rate, and sample size. The choice of the column type, column packing, and operating conditions are to a large degree based on prior experience and not on theoretical considerations. To some extent, GC is as much an art as it is a science.

When using gas chromatography, the sample to be analyzed is injected into a heated region of the gas chromatograph, where it is vaporized and carried by a flow of helium onto the column (see Figure 6-4). The components in the mixture are partially dissolved by the liquid phase on the column in a selective manner and, thus, move with the helium along the column at different rates. As they emerge from the column, they pass through a detector block, which is sensitive to small variations in thermal conductivity.

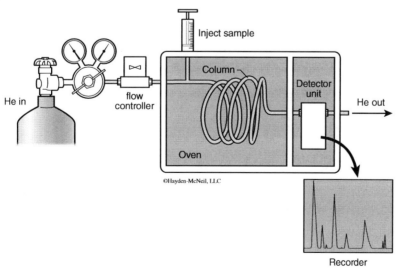

©Hayden-McNeil, LLC

Figure 6-4. *Schematic Representation of a Gas Chromatograph.*

Signals from the detector are recorded to give a record of the response which is proportional to the amount of material coming from the column. This recorder tracing has units of time (see Figure 6-5).

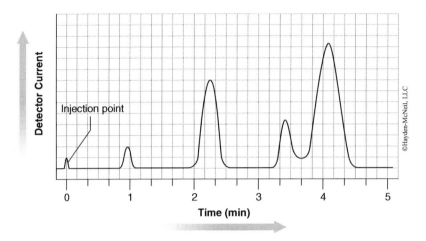

Figure 6-5. *A Typical Gas Chromatogram.*

Liquid phases are usually classified by their polarity. Some well-known phases that are commonly used are:

Nonpolar	
Nujol	A mineral oil, stable up to 200°C.
Apiezon	A family of hydrocarbon greases of varying molecular weights stable up to 250–300°C and typically used to separate hydrocarbon mixtures.
SE-30	A cross-linked methyl silicone rubber stable up to 350°C and often used to separate mixtures of either pesticides and/or steroids.
Medium Polar	
DC-200	A silicone oil polymer stable up to 200°C, which has found use in separating mixtures containing aldehydes and ketones.
Polar	
Carbowax	Polyethylene glycol polyethers stable up to 250°C, useful with mixtures of alcohols and ethers.
DEGS	Diethylene glycol succinate polyester stable up to 225°C and useful with esters and carboxylic acids.

While liquid phases have been found useful for specific classes of compounds, they are by no means limited in their usefulness to these classes alone. Indeed, one often can adapt a stationary phase and liquid phase in conjunction with machine settings to do virtually any separation.

The controls on a gas chromatograph allow one to select the flow rate of the carrier gas and the temperatures of the column, inlet port, and detector block. The magnitude of the electrical response is scaled by adjusting an attenuation control. The baseline on the chart paper is brought to the desired position with the "zero" control.

These many interdependent variables must be selected so that the gas chromatograph gives optimum performance as judged by two principal criteria. The first is related to peak broadening: the narrower the peak representing one substance, the more efficient the column under the given set of operating conditions. The second criterion concerns the degree to which two components are separated in the chromatogram. The further apart the peaks appear from one another on the chromatogram, the more efficient the column under the given set of operating conditions.

The injection port must be hot enough to vaporize the injected sample quickly, yet cool enough to avoid thermal decomposition of the components being analyzed. The column must be hot enough to give reasonably sharp peaks and a rapid analysis, yet cool enough to separate the components. The detector is maintained at a constant temperature hot enough to prevent condensation of material passing through the block. Then, the flow rate must be adjusted for maximum separation in the minimum amount of time.

Your instructor will most likely adjust the chromatograph to give the best separation for the experiment assigned to let you become familiar with the instrument. You should record the rate of helium flow (in mL per minute), the temperatures of the injection port, detector, and column, and the type of column being used. These settings, along with the retention times and identities of the peaks eluted, help to form a foundation for the future use of this instrument.

Retention times are most conveniently measured either in seconds or minutes, although centimeters of chart paper will do as well. When an injection of sample is made, a mark is made immediately at the point where the pen was at the time of injection. The retention time is then the time (or distance) from this point to the centerline of the peak. A typical gas chromatogram of a sample mixture is shown in Figure 6-5.

The response of the detector to a compound is usually proportional to the amount of compound passing through the detector. The amount of each component is therefore proportional to its relative peak area. A good approximation of peak areas can be obtained in the following manner: measure the height of the peak (h) and divide by two. Now measure the width of the peak at h/2 ($W_{h/2}$). The area of the peak is then $h \times W_{h/2}$. Other ways to measure the relative amount of each component include cutting out the peaks and weighing them, counting squares on the chart paper, using a planimeter, or—easiest of all (but most expensive)—using an electronic integrator which has been attached to the recorder or directly to the chromatograph.

The method most commonly employed in the student laboratory to determine percent composition of a mixture is illustrated in Figure 6-6.

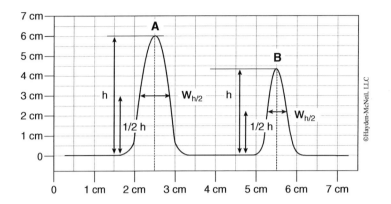

Figure 6-6. *Determination of Peak Area from $W_{h/2} \times h$.*

In the example shown, peak A has a height of 6.50 cm, and the width at half-height is 0.40 cm for an area of 2.6 cm². Peak B is 4.40 cm in height and 0.35 cm wide at half-height, for an area of 1.5 cm². The total area of the eluted peaks is 4.1 cm². Therefore,

$$\text{Peak A is then: } \frac{2.6 \text{ cm}^2}{4.1 \text{ cm}^2} \times 100 = 63\% \text{ of the mixture}$$

$$\text{and Peak B is: } \frac{1.5 \text{ cm}^2}{4.1 \text{ cm}^2} \times 100 = 37\% \text{ of the mixture}$$

Part 1: Thin Layer Chromatography

Review the discussion of thin layer chromatography before proceeding with this experiment. Remember that the overall process of TLC consists of applying a small droplet of a dilute solution of the mixture near one end of the slide, developing the chromatogram with solvent, then observing the results by a visualization technique. The ratio of the distance that a substance has moved to the distance traversed by the solvent is called the R_f value for the compound. R_f values can aid in the identification of substances when measurements are made under the same conditions; this usually means carrying out comparative chromatograms at the same time. Various features of a TLC plate are shown in the following diagram:

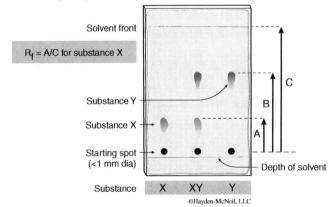

Recall that for good separation of components in the mixture, the solvent should be polar enough so that the components move from the origin, but not so polar that they move with the solvent front. Also, if a single solvent does not give a good separation of components, a solvent mixture may work better.

To visualize spots after the elution is complete, we will use two techniques. First, looking at the slide under an ultraviolet light will show any compounds that absorb ultraviolet light, for example, compounds containing benzene rings or conjugated systems. Next, placing the slide in an iodine chamber allows iodine to collect on the spots by a weak electronic interaction. This will cause the spots to appear dark brown. If the slide is removed from the chamber, however, the iodine will sublime off over the course of a few minutes, and the spots will "disappear."

THE EXPERIMENT

This exercise is a simple demonstration of TLC to provide practice in the technique. Although you may need more plates to complete the exercise, for the sake of efficiency, each student should start with four plates at one time.

Make 4–5 capillary spotters as shown in Figure 6-7 and prepare the developing chamber.

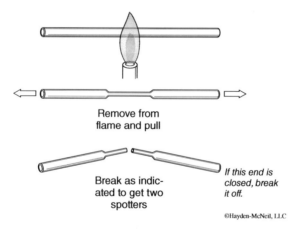

Remove from flame and pull

Break as indic-
ated to get two
spotters

If this end is
closed, break
it off.

©Hayden-McNeil, LLC

Figure 6-7.

You will need to use caution in applying the sample to the TLC plate since the dried silica gel surface can easily be dislodged. The liquid level in the developing chamber is also very important. If there is too much of the solvent at the bottom of the chamber, it will flood the applied spots and wash the material off the plate. On the other hand, if there is insufficient solvent to make adequate contact with the silica gel on the plate, the solvent will not travel up the plate. Exercise caution when placing the plate into the chamber and also when removing it. Try to remove the plate from the chamber as soon as the solvent has reached the line at the top. Let the developed plate dry before attempting to examine it closely as the silica gel surface is easily damaged when wet.

NOTE: *It is much easier to see than to explain how to prepare the spotters, prepare the chamber, and apply spots to the plates. Your instructor, therefore, will demonstrate these techniques.*

1.   *TLC Analysis of a Mixture of Colored Compounds*

You will be analyzing chromatograms of the following colored compounds:

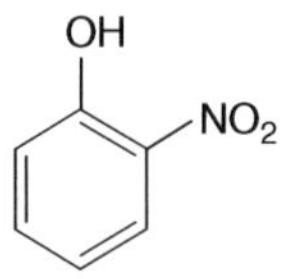

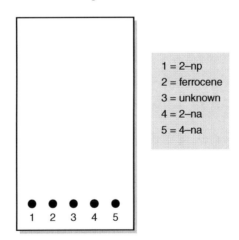

2–nitrophenol
(2–np)

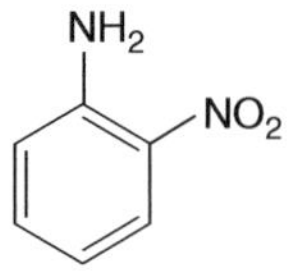

2–nitroaniline
(2–na)

4–nitroaniline
(4–na)

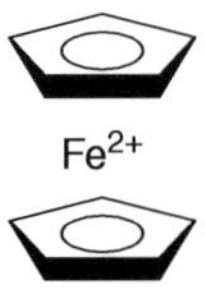

Ferrocene

For your initial analysis, spot your unknown and the colored standard compounds on one plate as shown in the diagram below:

1 = 2–np
2 = ferrocene
3 = unknown
4 = 2–na
5 = 4–na

1   2   3   4   5

Develop the plate using a 2:1 mixture of hexane and ether. Your unknown may contain two or three of the standard compounds. Draw a replica (to scale) of this plate in your Results section. Calculate the R_f value of each spot and record them as well. From your results, choose the compounds which appear to make up your mixture. If the choice is unclear, consult your instructor.

Next, spot a plate with the standards which you have chosen, your unknown, and a mixture of the standards prepared by spotting them one over the other. Develop the plate and draw a replica of it in your Results section. When you are sure of the identities of the compounds in your unknown mixture, calculate the R_f value for all spots on the last plate. Record these values as well as a replica of the TLC plate.

NOTE: *If you have problems, you may require more plates than those described above. If so, record information only for those plates which run properly and contribute to your determination of the identity of the components of your unknown mixture. Also, some compounds may streak when run on TLC plates. If they do so consistently, this is useful descriptive information about the spots that can be used to help identify the compounds.*

2. **TLC Analysis of Analgesic Drugs**

Analgesics, compounds that relieve pain, range from aspirin to morphine and related narcotics. In addition to aspirin, several other chemically similar compounds are widely used in nonprescription analgesic tablets. Among these are acetaminophen, ibuprofen, and salicylamide. Caffeine is sometimes added to these formulations to overcome drowsiness. Other ingredients may be added for different therapeutic effects, such as an antispasmodic or compounds that have a slight sedative action. In addition to the active ingredients, the tablets contain other substances that act as binders or enhance dissolution.

In this experiment, you will obtain as an unknown an over-the-counter analgesic drug. You are to identify the unknown drug by TLC comparison with these known reference compounds: aspirin (acetylsalicylic acid), acetaminophen (4'-acetamidophenol or 4'-hydroxyacetanilide), and caffeine. Your unknown analgesic will be one of those listed below; the chemical structures of the ingredients follow.

Drug	Ingredients
Anacin	Aspirin and caffeine
Bayer aspirin	Aspirin
Excedrin	Acetaminophen, aspirin, and caffeine
Tylenol	Acetaminophen

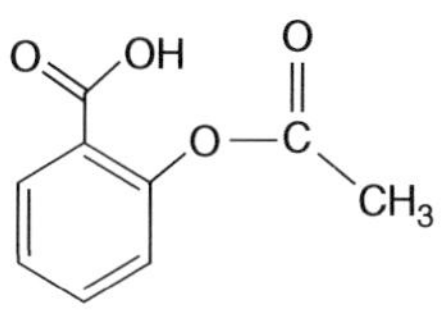

Aspirin 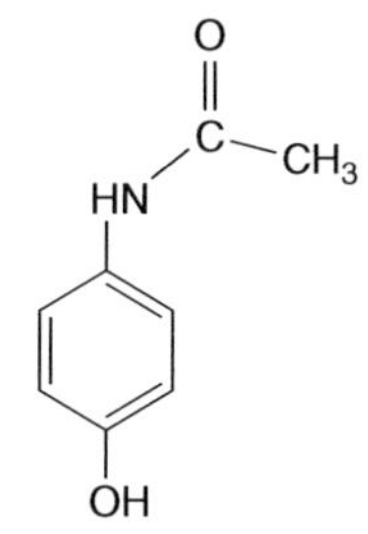   Acetaminophen 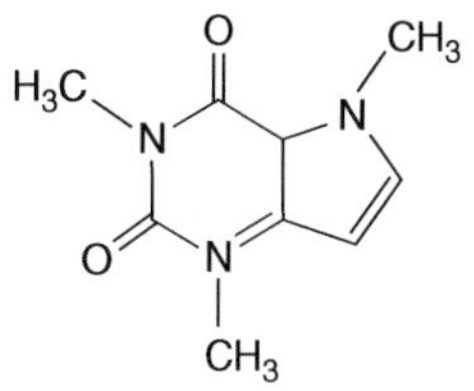   Caffeine

Procedure

Obtain a tablet of your unknown analgesic drug and samples (a few drops) of solutions of the three reference compounds. Record your unknown number.

Crush the analgesic tablet on some filter paper, and place the powder in a 6-inch test tube. Add 1 mL of a 1:1 CH_2Cl_2:methanol mixture, place the tube in a warm water bath in the hood, heat *gently* and stir the mixture for several minutes. Do not heat the solution so as to cause the dichloromethane to boil away! While not all of the tablet will dissolve (the tablet may also contain insoluble binders and inorganic buffering agents), enough will go into solution to spot the TLC plate.

Spot the known compounds and the unknown analgesic on a TLC plate as you did with the colored compounds.

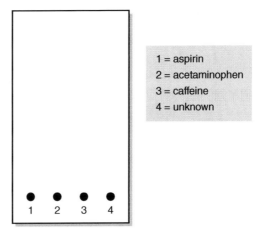

Develop the plate using a solvent mixture having the composition:

$$CH_2Cl_2\text{:methanol:acetic acid (80:4:1).}$$

> **NOTE TO INSTRUCTOR:** *The 80:4:1 solvent ratio is critical. This solution must therefore be fresh to ensure the correct solvent composition. Otherwise, separation will suffer.*

Examine the plate under UV light to see the components as dark spots against the fluorescent background. Outline the spots with a pencil. Then visualize the spots in an iodine chamber, as demonstrated by your instructor. Draw a replica of the plate in your Results section.

Identify your unknown as you did with your colored unknown. Be sure to determine the R_f's of all compounds involved.

If your unknown analgesic contains more than one compound, you should also run another TLC plate spotted with the unknown, each of the suspected knowns, and a mixture of the knowns prepared as before by spotting the knowns one over the other. Visualize the spots as before and record a replica of this plate in your Results section.

Discussion and Conclusions

1. Identify the components of your mixture of colored compounds, and, in two sentences, explain the basis for your conclusion.

2. Identify your unknown analgesic drug, and, in two sentences, explain the basis for your conclusion.

3. On the basis of the results of your TLC analysis, list the analgesic standard compounds in order of decreasing polarity. In one sentence, explain your reasoning.

Part 2: Column Chromatography

Review the discussion of column chromatography before proceeding with this experiment. Remember that the overall process of **column chromatography** consists of applying a solution of a mixture of compounds to be separated to the top of a vertical glass column that is packed with an adsorbent (the stationary phase). The mixture is washed down the column with solvent (the mobile phase) by gravity flow. The components of the mixture move down the column at different rates depending on their relative adsorptivities to the stationary phase. The choice of stationary phase and mobile phase is governed by the same factors which apply to TLC. Typical practice is to start with fairly nonpolar solvents to elute poorly adsorbed analytes and switch to successively more polar solvents (or mixtures of solvents) to remove the more strongly adsorbed components. In contrast to thin layer chromatography, rather than *developing* the chromatographic plate until the solvent front reaches the end of the plate, the mobile phase is passed through the column until the components of interest *elute* from the column. This results in individual bands of the eluting compounds (compare this to the individual spots on a TLC plate) which come off of the column at different times, thereby resulting in a physical separation of the components of the mixture. The separated components of the mixture can be isolated by evaporation of the elution solvent. Progress of the chromatographic separation can be monitored by analyzing individual elution fractions by TLC as they wash off the column. One of the major advantages of column chromatography is that the purification of compounds thus obtained is very high compared to alternative techniques such as recrystallization and distillation.

PREPARATION OF A COLUMN

Obtain a chromatography column suitable for the amount of adsorbent required in the experiment, and secure it to a ring stand with a clamp. Close the stopcock and fill the column 2/3 full of hexane (unless the experiment calls for another solvent to be used). Do not fill to the very top; there must be room for a powder funnel to fit into the top of the column without the tip of the funnel coming in contact with the liquid. With the help of a long glass rod, insert a small plug of glass wool or cotton into the top of the column, and push it down to the bottom. This serves to hold the adsorbent and prevents any solid from getting into the stopcock. Pour in 1/4–1/2 inch of clean sand. Weigh out the amount of adsorbent, and pour it slowly into the powder funnel so that it settles slowly through the solvent in the column and falls to the bottom. The level of the liquid in the column will rise because of the addition of the solid material and must be watched and continuously lowered to prevent the tip of the funnel from becoming wet.

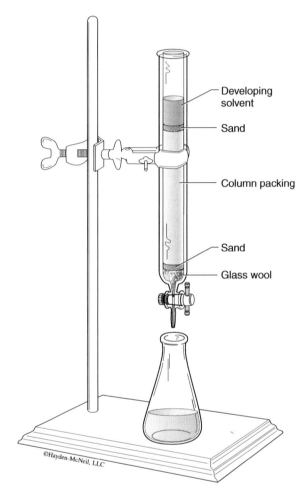

Figure 6-8. *Column Chromatography.*

While the adsorbent is settling to the bottom, it is helpful to tap the side of the column gently with the fingers, a cork ring, or a piece of thick-walled tubing to help release trapped air bubbles and to help settle the bed uniformly. After all of the adsorbent has been introduced and has settled, add an additional 1/4 inch of sand to the top of the bed. The solvent should now be run down to just above the top of the bed.

Procedure

The instructor will assign each student to do *one* of the following two separations.

Part A: Separation of a Fluorene/Fluorenone Mixture

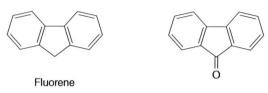

Fluorene

Fluorenone

Fluorene is a colorless solid, and fluorenone has a light yellow color. A fluorene/fluorenone mixture will be separated by adsorbing the material that has been dissolved in a small amount of toluene onto an alumina column, and then eluting the column with a sequence of solvents of increasing polarity. The solvents used for eluting the adsorbed material will be collected in numbered fractions, the solvent evaporated, and the residue examined and identified. Fluorene, the less polar hydrocarbon, will be eluted first while fluorenone, a ketone that is the more polar of the two compounds, will be eluted in later fractions. In the present experiment, the fluorene will be eluted with hexane and the fluorenone with a 9:1 hexane-acetone mixture.

> **IMPORTANT:** *When packing and running your column, you must not allow the solvent to drain below the sand. Doing so will allow air to get into the column and will adversely affect the separation in two ways:*

> (1) Component bands will not be sharply defined and may overlap, and (2) the rate of solvent flow will drop to a very slow rate—too slow to be able to finish the experiment in the allotted time. If either of these things happens, you may have to empty the column and start the experiment over again!

1. Prepare a column as described previously.

   Use 6 inches of alumina.

2. Weigh out **about 0.2 grams** of the fluorene/fluorenone mixture, and dissolve it in a minimum amount of toluene (0.5 mL of toluene should be enough). Crushing the solid with the tip of a glass rod and warming the flask in the palm of your hand will speed up dissolution.

3. Run the level of the solvent to slightly below the top of the sand and immediately apply the solution of sample to the column with a Pasteur pipet as demonstrated by your instructor.

4. Drain a small amount of solvent to bring the sample just below the top of the sand and onto the alumina bed.

5. Carefully fill the column with hexane without dislodging the sand or alumina, and begin to elute.

6. From time to time, collect a drop of eluant on a watch glass, and evaporate it. The presence or absence of solid residue will indicate presence/absence of fluorene. Collect the eluant in a waste beaker until the fluorene appears.

7. When fluorene appears, begin to collect the eluant in a flask labeled "Fraction #1."

8. When essentially all of the fluorene has been eluted (as evidenced by the watch glass test), switch to the waste beaker and run the solvent down to the top of the sand. Again, empty the waste beaker into the waste solvent drum.

9. Now, elute the column with a 9:1 hexane/acetone mixture. Be sure to *save* the eluant that you collect in the waste beaker.

10. When you see a defined yellow band of fluorenone in the column, change the solvent to acetone (remember the present solvent must be run down to the top of the sand before changing solvent). When the yellow band reaches the top of the glass wool plug, collect the eluant in a flask labeled "fraction #2" and continue to elute until all of the fluorenone has been removed.

11. Run a TLC—applying five spots: Fraction #1, Fraction #2, the contents of the waste beaker, and samples of each of the pure compounds (*i.e.*, standards). Analyze the results of your separation by column chromatography (success or failure) by analyzing what you see on the TLC plate.

    NOTE: *The developing solvent for the TLC should be 9:1 hexane/ether.*

When the chromatography is finished, clean the column before the alumina forms a hard cake. Follow the instructor's demonstration on how to empty the column to avoid breaking it.

Used alumina and solvents must be placed in the waste containers specified by your instructor. They are *not* to be placed in the trash cans!

Part B: Separation of a Mixture of Nitroaniline Isomers

In last week's experiment, we observed that the isomers of nitroaniline could be separated and identified using TLC on a silica gel substrate and developed with a mixture of hexane and diethyl ether mixed in the approximate ratio of 2:1.

Today, we will attempt to separate the nitroaniline isomers by adsorbing a mixture of *ortho-* and *para*-nitroaniline on an alumina column. Elution of the materials will require the use of more than one solvent for effective separation. In order to analyze the samples that you will elute from the column, you will still use the silica gel substrate for your TLC plates and the hexane-diethyl ether solvent mixture.

IMPORTANT: *When packing and running your column, you must not allow the solvent to drain below the sand. Doing so will allow air to get into the column and will adversely affect the separation in two ways:*

(1) Component bands will not be sharply defined and may overlap, and (2) the rate of solvent flow will drop to a very slow rate—too slow to be able to finish the experiment in the allotted time. If either of these things happens, you may have to empty the column and start the experiment over again!

1. Prepare a column as described previously.

   Use 7 inches of alumina.

2. Weigh out about **0.05 grams each** of *ortho-* and *para*-nitroaniline and dissolve them together in the smallest possible amount of acetone (1/2 mL should be enough solvent). Use a stirring rod to crush and grind the solids so that they will dissolve more readily. *Remember that the nitroanilines are somewhat toxic—avoid getting them on your hands.*

3. Run the solvent to just below the top of the sand on the column, and carefully apply the solution of nitroanilines to the column with a Pasteur pipet as demonstrated by your instructor.

4. Drain a small amount of solvent to bring the sample just below the top of the sand and onto the alumina bed. (If traces of the nitroanilines are clinging to the column exposed above the sand, it may be necessary to wash them down with **a few drops** of diethyl ether. See your instructor for help with this.)

5. Without disturbing the sand or alumina, carefully fill the column with hexane and elute into a waste beaker. When enough hexane has been run through the column, the bands of yellow which have been steadily moving down the column will become stationary, and the polarity of the eluting solvent must be increased.

6. Run the hexane to the top of the sand and switch to a 9:1 mixture of hexane/acetone.

7. When the first yellow color reaches the top of the glass wool plug, begin to collect the eluant in a flask labeled "Fraction #1." Collect until essentially all of the first band of color has been removed and then switch to a 5:1 hexane/acetone solvent system.

8. As soon the first band of color is removed, run the solvent down to the top of the sand and switch to pure acetone. Meanwhile, collect the solvent (either colorless or slightly yellow) that elutes between the two colored bands into a fresh beaker, and *save it*. Switch to a flask labeled "Fraction #2" as soon as the second band of color reaches the top of the glass wool, or when the eluant becomes deep yellow again.

9. Run a TLC—applying five spots: Fraction #1, Fraction #2, the contents of the waste beaker, and samples of each of the pure compounds (*i.e.,* standards). Analyze the results of your separation by column chromatography (success or failure) by analyzing what you see on the TLC plate.

The developing solvent will be the same as that used in the TLC experiment.

When the chromatography is finished, clean the column before the alumina forms a hard cake. Follow the instructor's demonstration on how to empty the column to avoid breaking it.

Used alumina and solvents must be placed in the waste containers specified by your instructor. They are *not* to be placed in the trash cans!

Part C: Separation of a Mixture of Ferrocene and Acetyl Ferrocene

1. Prepare a column as described previously.

   Use 6 inches of alumina.

2. Weigh out 0.05 g of each of ferrocene and acetyl ferrocene and dissolve them together in the smallest possible amount of CH_2Cl_2 (0.5 mL should be enough solvent).

3. Run the solvent to just below the top of the sand in the column, and carefully apply the solution of ferrocenes as demonstrated by your instructor.

4. Drain a small amount of solvent to bring the sample just below the top of the sand and into the column bed.

5. Without disturbing the sand or alumina, carefully fill the column with hexane and elute into a waste beaker, change the receiver to your first labeled beaker (Fraction #1) when the first colored band is about 1 cm from the bottom of the column.

6. Change the eluting solvent to 1:1 hexane-TBME (t-butyl methyl ether). Fill the column with this mixed solvent to elute most of the first band (Fraction #1).

7. Change the eluting solvent to pure TBME. Collect this intermediate fraction in a labeled beaker (Fraction #2). When the second colored band is about 1 cm from the bottom of the column, place a labeled beaker (Fraction #3).

8. Change the eluting solvent to acetone. Elute the entire second band with acetone (Fraction #3).

9. Run TLC applying five spots: Fraction #1, Fraction #2, Fraction #3, and samples of each of the pure compounds. Analyze the results of your separation by column chromatography (success or failure) by analyzing what you see on the TLC plate.

Questions

1. Why is it important to apply the sample to the column in the smallest amount of solvent possible? What do you think would have happened if you had used too much solvent in this step?

2. What is the purpose of the sand on the top of the column? On the bottom of the column?

3. Now that you have experienced both techniques, *compare and contrast* melting point determination and TLC as methods for detecting impurities in a solid sample? Explain your answer.

4. An orange compound, dissolved in dichloromethane, is added to a chromatography column. The elution is begun using hexane as the solvent. After 6 L of solvent was passed through the column, the orange band had still not traveled down the column appreciably. What should be done to make this experiment work better.

5. A sample was placed on a chromatography column. Dichloromethane was used as the eluting solvent. No separation of the components in the sample was observed. What might have gone wrong? How would you change the experiment in order to overcome this problem?

CHAPTER 7

Steam Distillation—
The Isolation of Eugenol from Cloves

When a mixture of two **miscible** liquids such as cyclohexane and toluene is distilled, the boiling point of this mixture is between the boiling points of each of the pure components. By contrast, if a mixture of two **immiscible** liquids such as benzene and water is distilled, the boiling point of the mixture will be found to be *below* the boiling point of each pure component. Since the two liquids are essentially insoluble in each other, the benzene molecules in a droplet of benzene are not diluted by water molecules from nearby water droplets, and hence the vapor pressure exerted by the benzene is the same as that of benzene alone at the existing temperature. The same is true of the water present.

Because they are immiscible, the two liquids independently exert pressures against the atmosphere. Therefore, boiling occurs when the sum of the two partial pressures equals the atmospheric pressure. The result is that *such a mixture boils at a temperature that is lower than the boiling point of either pure substance*. This fact has proven especially useful in the purification and isolation of substances with very high boiling points that can decompose if exposed to the high heat necessary for distillation. Such a substance, if it is insoluble in water and does not undergo chemical reaction with water, can be distilled along with water. The resulting mixture of substance and water will distill at a temperature that is slightly below 100° at 1 atmosphere. This process is therefore called **steam distillation**. Many compounds can be purified under these very mild conditions. For example, naphthalene, a solid that boils at 218°C, distills with water below 100°C.

ISOLATION OF EUGENOL FROM CLOVES

Introduction

For centuries people have isolated so-called "essential oils" from plant material. Some of these substances are still used for medicinal purposes. Among these are camphor, quinine, oil of cloves, cedarwood oil, turpentine, cinnamon, gum benzoin, and myrrh. Oil of cloves, which consists almost entirely of eugenol and its acetate, is a food flavoring agent as well as a dental anesthetic. The Food and Drug Administration had declared clove oil to be "the most effective nonprescription remedy for toothache."

Eugenol   Acetyleugenol

Cloves are the flower buds from a tropical tree that grows in the Spice Islands of Indonesia and the islands of the Indian Ocean. A single tree can yield up to 75 lb of the hand picked, sun-dried buds that we know as cloves.

Cloves contain between 14% and 20% by weight of essential oil, of which about half can be isolated. The principal constituents of clove oil are eugenol and its acetyl derivative. Eugenol boils at 255°C, but being insoluble in water, will steam distill at a temperature slightly below the boiling point of water. Being a phenol, eugenol will dissolve in aqueous alkali to form its conjugate base (a phenolate ion). This forms the basis for its separation from its acetyl derivative.

Eugenol

Procedure
Place 25 g of whole cloves in a 250 mL round-bottom flask, add 100 mL of water, and set up as you would for a simple distillation. Heat the flask strongly—using a heating mantle as the heat source (set the Variac to 70–80%)—until boiling starts; then reduce the heat just enough to prevent foam from being carried over into the receiver. Since foaming is a potential problem, use an Erlenmeyer flask as the distillation receiver, and transfer the distillate periodically to a graduated cylinder so that you can keep track of the volume that distills over. This way, if any material does foam over, the entire distillate will not be contaminated. Collect 50 mL of distillate, lower the heating mantle, and add 60 mL of water to the distilling flask. Resume the distillation, and collect an additional 50 mL of distillate.

The eugenol is very sparingly soluble in water and is easily extracted from the distillate with dichloromethane. Place the 100 mL of distillate in a 250 mL separatory funnel, and extract successively (remember what this means!) with *three* 15 mL portions of dichloromethane. (Which will be the CH_2Cl_2 layer?)

> **NOTE:** *In this extraction, very gentle shaking will fail to remove all of the product, while long, vigorous shaking will produce an emulsion of the organic layer and water.*

The separatory funnel may appear to have three layers in it; this is actually two layers plus the emulsion between them. It is better to err on the side of vigorous shaking and draw off the clear, lower layer to the emulsion line for the first two extractions. For the third extraction, shake the mixture less vigorously, and allow a longer period of time for the two layers to separate.

Combine the three dichloromethane extracts (the aqueous layer can be discarded), and add just enough anhydrous calcium chloride pellets so that the drying agent no longer clumps together but appears to be a dry powder as it settles to the bottom of the flask. This may require as little as 2 g of drying agent. Swirl the flask for a minute or two to complete the drying process, and then decant the solvent into a *tared* Erlenmeyer flask. It is quite easy to decant the dichloromethane from the drying agent, and therefore it will not be necessary to set up a filtration apparatus for this separation.

Add a boiling chip or a wood boiling stick (easier to remove than a boiling chip), and evaporate the solution on a hot water bath in the hood. From its weight, calculate the total yield of crude clove oil isolated.

Analysis of the Eugenol/Acetyleugenol

1. *Thin Layer Chromatography (TLC)*

Analyze your product by TLC. To do so, apply four different spots, side-by-side, on a TLC plate as follows: (1) a known sample of eugenol, (2) a known sample of acetyleugenol, (3) a spot of (1) *directly on top* of a spot of (2) (this will tell you what a mixture of the two compounds would look like), and (4) a spot of your steam distilled clove oil (place 1 or 2 drops in ~1 mL of dichloromethane—don't spot the neat liquid!). Use ether-hexane (1:2) as your eluting solvent. Make sure that the spots are very small. After elution, visualize the spots—first with the UV lamp and then with iodine. Be sure to draw a replica of your TLC plate in your notebook.

> **NOTE:** *If the compounds do not separate distinctly, prepare and elute another TLC plate—this time making sure that the spotting solutions are as dilute as possible and that the spots are very small. This is to ensure that the plate is not overloaded with material.*

2. Chemical Tests

Eugenol contains two functional groups which can be tested for by classical chemical methods.

a. Ferric Chloride (FeCl₃) Test for Phenols

To a test tube containing approximately 0.5 mL of ethanol, add a drop or two of the clove oil. Then add one or two drops of ferric chloride solution. Record your observations. An intense red, blue, purple, or green coloration is considered a positive test for a phenol.

b. Baeyer Test for Unsaturation (Alkenes)

One of the characteristic properties of alkenes and alkynes is the addition of electrophiles to the π-bond. This reaction is quite simple and is often used as a test for the identification of unsaturated hydrocarbons.

Dissolve a small amount of the clove oil in 2 mL of acetone in a test tube. Add 2% $KMnO_4$ solution one drop at a time. Shake the test tube vigorously after the addition of each drop. If the purple color of the permanganate ion disappears immediately after the addition of two drops of reagent, the presence of an alkene is indicated. In addition to the disappearance of the purple color, there will usually be a brown precipitate of MnO_2. At times, the MnO_2 will remain suspended, and a reddish-brown color will gradually replace the purple color.

3. Infrared (IR) Spectroscopy

Infrared spectra can be run on neat (undiluted) liquids. Since glass is opaque to infrared radiation, the sample for infrared spectroscopy is placed between sodium chloride plates. The sodium chloride plates are brittle and, if dropped, crack easily. They can also be attacked by moisture, so *handle only by the edges*. Each plate costs more than you might expect, and you may be held responsible for their replacement if damaged.

To run an IR spectrum of a neat (and free of water! Why?) liquid, remove two salt plates from the desiccator, and place them on a soft Kimwipe rather than on the hard bench top. Place a drop of the liquid on one of the plates. Place the other plate on top and press down gently using a Kimwipe in order to create a thin, uniform film between the plates. Wipe any excess sample from the edges. Place the plates in the holder, followed by the rubber gasket, and finally the metal face plate. Next, put on all three of the nuts and *gently* tighten them to apply an even pressure to the top plate. Too much pressure will cause the brittle plates to crack.

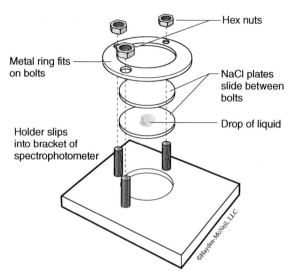

Figure 7-1. *Assembly of Liquid Sample between NaCl Plates.*

Follow your instructor's instructions for how to use the FT-IR spectrophotometer, and run an infrared spectrum of your sample of eugenol. Compare this spectrum with the spectrum of an authentic sample of eugenol (Figure 7-2).

When you have completed taking your spectrum, remove the salt plates from the holder, carefully wipe off your sample with a Kimwipe, and rinse the plates with solvent (*dry, reagent-grade* acetone or dichloromethane). Dry the plates and *return them to the desiccator*. **Do not leave them out in the room.**

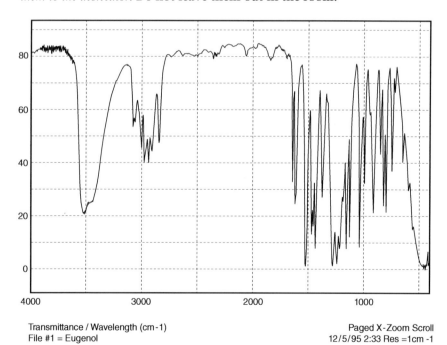

Transmittance / Wavelength (cm-1)   Paged X-Zoom Scroll
File #1 = Eugenol   12/5/95 2:33 Res =1cm -1

Figure 7-2. *Infrared Spectrum of Eugenol (thin film).*

CHAPTER 8

Dehydration of 2-Methylcyclohexanol—Synthesis, Distillation, and Gas Chromatography

You will use several techniques in this experiment: fractional distillation, extraction, and gas chromatography are three of the more important ones.

The equation and the mechanism for this reaction are given below. You will have your first experience dealing with experimental losses during this experiment. Make note of these as you feel they are occurring. This reaction does not go entirely to completion, and there are minor side reactions that occur. By careful attention to technique, you will be able to minimize mechanical losses, but keep in mind there is no such thing as 100% yield.

Overall Reaction:

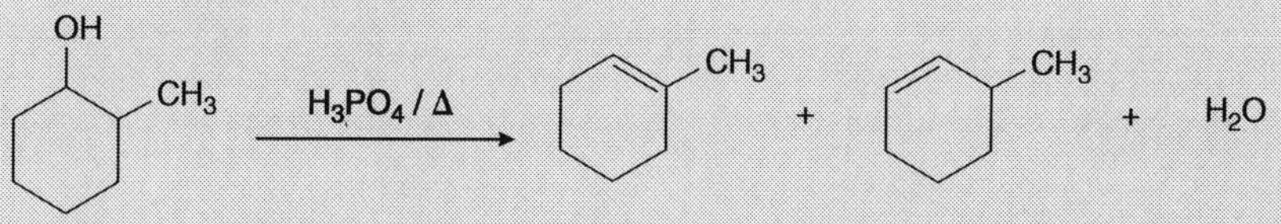

$$\text{(2-methylcyclohexanol)} \xrightarrow{H_3PO_4 / \Delta} \text{(1-methylcyclohexene)} + \text{(3-methylcyclohexene)} + H_2O$$

Mechanism:

1–Methylcyclohexene   3–Methylcyclohexene

83

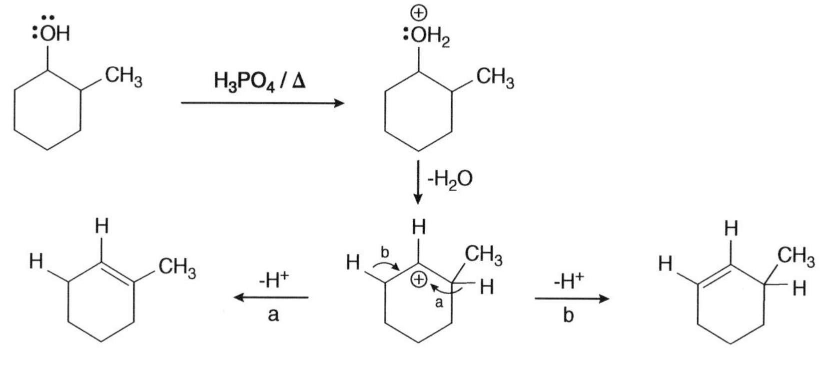

EXPERIMENTAL PROCEDURE

Assemble a fractional distillation apparatus (refer to the appropriate diagram in the Distillation Experiment). For this experiment the receiver must be a round-bottom flask. Add 10 mL of 2-methylcyclohexanol into a 50 mL round-bottom flask. Then add about 3 mL of 85% phosphoric acid and several boiling stones.

> **NOTE:** *The phosphoric acid is a catalyst and does not enter into the yield calculation.*

Attach the flask to the distillation apparatus, and, using a heating mantle as the heat source, begin to heat it slowly. When the contents have begun to boil, watch the vapor ring. It should rise slowly, and the thermometer reading should equilibrate somewhere between 85–100°C. Continue distilling until about 9–10 mL of liquid have been collected or until the distilling flask becomes foggy.

> **NOTE:** *Do not allow the round-bottom flask to dry out! Lower the heating mantle as soon as the required amount of distillate has been collected.*

Stopper the flask containing the distillate, and set it aside. Take the round-bottom distilling flask (*remember, it's hot*), and clamp it to the sink faucet. *Very carefully* add soap and water to the flask to dilute the residue so that it does not solidify when it cools.

Transfer the distillate to your separatory funnel using a few mL of water to complete the transfer, and draw down the water layer. (Which layer is it?) Test the water layer for acid with pH paper. If acid is present, wash the product layer with 3 mL of 10% sodium hydroxide solution, followed by 5 mL of water. (These are *successive* washings. Remember what that means!) If there is no acid present, transfer the product to a clean, dry Erlenmeyer flask of appropriate size (a "flask of appropriate size" is one which will hold all of the product and be 1/2 to 2/3 full), and remove the remaining water by swirling with anhydrous calcium chloride pellets (if you have about 10 mL of product, a teaspoon of $CaCl_2$ pellets should be adequate to remove all of the water).

While you are waiting for your product to dry, tare a clean 25 mL Erlenmeyer flask, and then clean your distillation apparatus. Filter or decant the dried product into the tared flask, and reweigh it to determine the grams of product obtained (decant means to pour the liquid slowly and carefully so as to leave the solid behind while transferring as much of the liquid as possible). Stopper the flask well to prevent evaporation of the volatile alkenes. Give your stoppered (and labeled) flask to your instructor for gas chromatographic analysis of your sample. Watch your instructor run your sample through the gas chromatograph.

Calculations

1. Obtain gas chromatograms of pure 1-methylcyclohexene and pure 3-methylcyclohexene from your instructor, and place them in your notebook. Measure the retention time of each alkene, and compare them with the retention times of your product mixture.

2. Identify each component in your chromatogram. Which isomer eluted first from the column? Which isomer came off second?

3. Calculate the percentage composition of the component peaks using the width at half-height [$h \times W_{h/2}$] method.

4. Calculate the overall theoretical and actual yields of your mixture of methylcyclohexenes, showing all work.

5. From the percentage composition of the mixture, calculate the actual yield in grams of each of the two methylcyclohexenes. Show all work.

Questions

1. Why was it necessary to wash the crude methylcyclohexenes with aqueous sodium bicarbonate solution?

2. List the manipulations where mechanical loss of product could have occurred.

3. Identities of the components in a mixture may be determined by a technique called **spiking**. Suppose you had run a gas chromatogram on your product and had then deliberately added a drop of a known sample of 3-methylcyclohexene to a drop of your product. What would you expect the new chromatogram to show you?

4. Do you consider this a good preparative procedure for making 3-methylcyclohexene? Why?

CHAPTER 9

**Nucleophilic Substitution Reactions I—
Mechanisms and Synthesis**

INTRODUCTION

The overall reaction in a nucleophilic substitution is as follows:

$$Nu^{\ominus} \quad + \quad RX \quad \longrightarrow \quad RNu \quad + \quad X^{\ominus}$$

This type of reaction can occur by either of two different mechanisms:

a. **Bimolecular Nucleophilic Substitution-S_N2:**

This is a **one-step** (concerted) process:

$$Nu^{\ominus} \quad + \quad R\!-\!X \quad \longrightarrow \quad R-Nu \quad + \quad X^{\ominus}$$

b. **Unimolecular Nucleophilic Substitution-S_N1:**

This is a **two-step** process in which the first step is the slow (rate-determining) step:

$$R\!-\!X \quad \underset{}{\overset{slow}{\rightleftharpoons}} \quad R^{\oplus} \quad + \quad :X^{\ominus} \quad \longrightarrow \quad R-Nu$$

$$Nu^{\ominus}$$

The following series of experiments will provide experience with both of these reaction types.

PART I: A SYNTHETIC APPLICATION OF NUCLEOPHILIC SUBSTITUTION

Tertiary alcohols can be converted to their corresponding *tert*-halides by S_N1 reactions. Shown here, *t*-butyl chloride (2-chloro-2-methylpropane) may be prepared from *t*-butyl alcohol by the following S_N1 reaction:

$$CH_3\!-\!\underset{\underset{CH_3}{|}}{\overset{\overset{CH_3}{|}}{C}}\!-\!OH \quad + \quad HCl \quad \longrightarrow \quad CH_3\!-\!\underset{\underset{CH_3}{|}}{\overset{\overset{CH_3}{|}}{C}}\!-\!Cl \quad + \quad H_2O$$

The mechanism for this S_N1 reaction is:

The important features of the route are:

a.   *t*-**Butyl alcohol, 2-methyl-2-propanol, is the substrate of this reaction.** The *t*-butyl group is ideal for the S_N1 mechanism, as it will produce a tertiary carbocation, the most stable alkyl carbocation, once the protonated OH group (*i.e.*, OH_2) leaves.

b.   **Hydrochloric acid (HCl) serves two purposes in this reaction:** It provides both the nucleophile ($Cl^{\ominus}$) and the proton catalyst which converts the OH group, a poor leaving group which cannot be displaced by $Cl^{\ominus}$, into H_2O, a much better leaving group.

PART II: A COMPARISON OF THE REACTIVITY OF ALKYL HALIDES

This part of the experiment is divided into two sections:

SECTION A of this experiment compares the reactivity of a variety of alkyl halides under S_N1-favored conditions. Solvolysis (an S_N1 reaction where the nucleophile is the solvent) in ethanol is carried out, and the reaction is followed via the precipitation of the halide ion leaving group as its silver salt.

$$R-X \; + \; Ag^{\oplus} \; \longrightarrow \; R^{\oplus} \; + \; AgX \; (precipitate)$$

In the S_N1 mechanism, the rate is dependent solely on the concentration of the alkyl halide. Two factors which can affect the rate must be considered:

a.   **The R group:** If the structure of R gives rise to a stable carbocation, RX should be a reactive substrate in an S_N1 mechanism.

b.   **The X group:** The better the leaving group, the faster the reaction rate under S_N1 conditions.

SECTION B of this experiment compares the reactivity of a variety of alkyl halides under conditions which favor the S_N2 mechanism (*i.e.*, using a polar, aprotic solvent, acetone, and a good nucleophile, $I^{\ominus}$).

$$Na^{\oplus} \; I^{\ominus} \; + \; R-X \; \xrightarrow{\text{acetone}} \; NaX \; + \; R-I \quad (X = Cl, Br)$$

In the S_N2 mechanism, the rate is proportional to both the concentration of RX and the nucleophile. Since the nucleophile will be the same for all reactions, only the structure of the substrate, RX, need be considered. The following factors will therefore be studied:

a. **The nature of the R group:** In the S_N2 mechanism, steric factors are important. Therefore, the size of the R group is important.

b. **The nature of X:** Just as in the S_N1 mechanism, the better the leaving group, the more reactive the alkyl halide will be in an S_N2 mechanism.

The reactions will be monitored by observing the precipitation of NaCl or NaBr, both of which are less soluble than NaI in acetone.

Procedure

Part 1—Synthesis: Preparation of tert-amyl chloride

Cool about 20 mL of concentrated hydrochloric acid (12 M HCl) in an ice bath. Add about 12 mL of *t*-amyl alcohol (2-methyl-2-butanol), and pour it into a separatory funnel. Slowly add the cooled HCl. Stopper the separatory funnel, and shake it in the proper manner for at least 10 minutes.

> **NOTE:** *Review the proper use of the separatory funnel from an earlier experiment. Do not forget to periodically release the pressure. Always point the funnel away from yourself or anyone in the vicinity.*

Allow the separatory funnel to rest on the iron ring until the alkyl halide layer separates. (Based on the densities of *t*-amyl chloride and water, which is the *t*-amyl chloride layer?)

Draw off the aqueous layer, and set it aside until the end of the experiment (to be safe). Wash the product (the *t*-amyl chloride) *successively* with about 10 mL of cold water, 10 mL of 5% sodium bicarbonate solution, and 10 mL of water. Draw off the *t*-amyl chloride into a stoppered, 125 mL Erlenmeyer flask, and dry it over anhydrous calcium chloride, $CaCl_2$, for at least 10 minutes.

Decant or filter the dried *t*-amyl chloride into a 100 mL round-bottom flask, and perform a simple distillation.

Collect the product in a pre-weighed flask over a $\pm 2°$ range of the *t*-amyl chloride boiling point. Record the boiling point range obtained.

Weigh the container plus the *t*-amyl chloride. Calculate the weight of *t*-amyl chloride and the percent yield. Submit the product to your instructor.

Part 2—Mechanism: Relative Reactivity of Alkyl Halides

Section A

Label six clean, dry test tubes from "1" to "6." Use the following alkyl halides, one in each test tube:

1. *n*-Butyl chloride (1-chlorobutane)

2. *sec*-Butyl chloride (2-chlorobutane)

3. *t*-Butyl chloride (2-chloro-2-methylpropane)

4. *n*-Butyl bromide (1-bromobutane)

5. Allyl chloride (3-chloropropene)

6. Chlorobenzene

Place about 4 mL of 2% ethanolic silver nitrate solution (2% $AgNO_3$ in ethanol) into each of the six test tubes. Add three drops of the appropriate alkyl halide to each test tube, and shake to mix the reagents thoroughly.

Note the exact time at which a precipitate is formed. After five minutes, heat those tubes containing unreacted halide in a beaker of water which is about 50–55°C. After twenty minutes, consider any unreacted halide as being completely unreactive.

Clean and dry the six test tubes before performing Section B.

Section B

Place about 2 mL of a 15% solution of NaI in acetone into each of the six test tubes. Add six drops of the appropriate alkyl halide (the same ones used in Section A) to each test tube. Shake thoroughly to mix the reagents. Observe at room temperature for five minutes, noting the time of appearance of any cloudy precipitate. This precipitate is harder to see than the one in Section A. Those tubes that show no reaction after five minutes should be heated as before. Be careful not to evaporate the solvent, or the reagent will precipitate and give a false result. After twenty minutes, add another 2 mL portion of the sodium iodide solution to those tubes showing no reaction. Several of the tubes may still show no reaction after a second 20-minute period.

Arrange the halides in order of reactivity under the two sets of conditions. Discuss the reasons for these observations in your notebook.

CHAPTER 10

Nucleophilic Substitution Reactions II—
The Kinetics of Solvolysis

INTRODUCTION

In the preceding experiment, we looked at the practical application of nucleophilic substitution reactions in synthesis. We also examined the rate at which various substrates react under S_N1 and S_N2 conditions. The rates were examined in a qualitative manner so that we could examine the effects of substrate structure. In this experiment, we are going to examine the rate of this reaction in a quantitative manner and look at some factors which affect the reaction rate.

The following factors will influence the rate of nucleophilic substitution of alkyl halides:

1. The structure of the alkyl halide, (*i.e.*, the nature of the alkyl group and the leaving group)

2. The solvent

3. The temperature

4. The concentrations of the reactants

We shall examine these effects by way of a simple process, unimolecular solvolysis. The term **solvolysis** means a reaction in which the solvent is also the nucleophile. The S_N1 reaction to be studied is the reverse of the one examined in the last experiment:

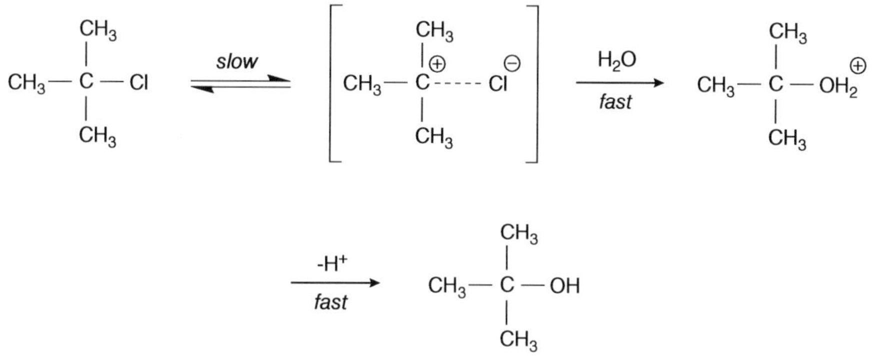

$$CH_3-\overset{\overset{\displaystyle CH_3}{|}}{\underset{\underset{\displaystyle CH_3}{|}}{C}}-Cl \quad \xrightleftharpoons{slow} \quad \left[CH_3-\overset{\overset{\displaystyle CH_3}{|}}{\underset{\underset{\displaystyle CH_3}{|}}{\overset{\oplus}{C}}}\text{-----}\overset{\ominus}{Cl} \right] \quad \xrightarrow[fast]{H_2O} \quad CH_3-\overset{\overset{\displaystyle CH_3}{|}}{\underset{\underset{\displaystyle CH_3}{|}}{C}}-\overset{\oplus}{O}H_2$$

$$\xrightarrow[fast]{-H^+} \quad CH_3-\overset{\overset{\displaystyle CH_3}{|}}{\underset{\underset{\displaystyle CH_3}{|}}{C}}-OH$$

The first step represents the breaking of the carbon-halogen bond of *t*-butyl chloride to form a reactive intermediate, a carbocation, and a chloride ion. The intermediate carbocation reacts very rapidly with water to form the alcohol product and acid (H^+). When a reaction goes through several steps, the rate of the slowest step determines the overall rate of the reaction. *This slowest step is called the rate-determining step.*

For the reaction of an alkyl halide with solvent, the rate law generally takes the form:

$$\text{Rate} = k[R - X] \tag{1}$$

This equation indicates that the rate of reaction is proportional to the first power of the concentration of the reactant (alkyl halide) and is consistent with the mechanism described above where the rate-determining step is unimolecular, (*i.e.*, involves only one molecule, the R – X). This reaction is said to be "first order with respect to the concentration of the alkyl halide." The rate constant, k, has the units of 1/time (sec^{-1}).

The rate law of a particular reaction and its corresponding rate constant, are generally found in the following way:

The differential equation for the rate expression is

$$-\frac{dc}{dt} = k[R - X] \tag{2}$$

in which [R–X] = concentration of the alkyl halide in moles/liter and t = time. The negative sign preceding the expression indicates that what is being measured is the decrease in the concentration of the reactant with time. One can also measure the increase in concentration of the product, in which case the sign of the expression would be positive. When equation (2) is integrated within the limits of C_0 at t = 0 and C_t at time = t, the desired relationship is obtained where

$$\ln\frac{C_0}{C_1} = kt \text{ or } 2.303 \log\frac{C_0}{C_1} = kt \tag{3}$$

where C_0 is the initial molar concentration of RX at the start of the reaction (t = 0) and C_t is the concentration at any elapsed time, t.

In this experiment, a solution of *t*-butyl chloride in acetone will be added to a solution of aqueous sodium hydroxide that contains bromophenol blue indicator. Bromophenol blue indicator is blue in basic medium and yellow in acid medium. The amount of hydroxide added (0.3 mL of 0.1 M solution) is equivalent to 10% of the total amount of alkyl chloride (3.0 mL of a 0.1 M solution). Solvolysis begins at the time of mixing and proceeds to yield the alcohol and H^+ at a characteristic rate. When the acid produced has neutralized the hydroxide present, the indicator changes from blue to yellow, and the time required for this change represents the time in which 10% of the reaction has occurred. The concentration factor C_0/C_t can then be expressed as:

$$\frac{1}{(1 - \% \text{ reaction}/100)} = \frac{C_0}{C_1} = 1.11 \tag{4}$$

Substituting this value into equation (3):

$$2.30 \log 1.11 = kt \tag{5}$$

$$2.30 \, (0.045) = kt \tag{6}$$

$$0.104 = kt \tag{7}$$

$$k = 0.104/t \tag{8}$$

Therefore, it follows from equation (8), that the rate constant is proportional to the time it takes for the color to change.

Procedure

Students will work in pairs assigned by the instructor. Be sure to indicate the name of your partner in your write-up. All calculations of the basic data, however, should be done by you individually.

Prepare a table with columns headed:

Trial   Time (sec)   Temp. (°C) k (sec^{-1}) k_{avg} Solvent Comp.

Obtain a *dry* 50 mL buret with a Teflon stopcock graduated in 0.1 mL increments, and fill it with a 0.1 M solution of *t*-butyl chloride in acetone. Obtain a 10 mL buret graduated in 0.05 mL increments, and fill it with 0.1 M sodium hydroxide solution. Obtain a 50 mL buret graduated in 0.1 mL increments, and fill it with deionized water.

Obtain six 25 or 50 mL Erlenmeyer flasks and make certain that they are clean and *dry*. Label three of the flasks as "Flask 1" and three of the flasks as "Flask 2" to be used for the **Standard Technique Method**.

Standard Technique Method

Flask 1

> Place 3 mL of the 0.1 M solution of *t*-butyl chloride in acetone into each of the three flasks labeled "Flask 1" (the *t*-butyl chloride is dissolved in acetone so that it will be miscible with water).

Flask 2

> Into each of the remaining three flasks, place 0.3 mL of the 0.1 M sodium hydroxide solution, 6.7 mL of water, and 4–5 drops of bromophenol blue indicator. Swirl to mix well.

Record the room temperature, note the time, and quickly but carefully pour the contents of Flask 1 into Flask 2. Swirl and immediately pour the solution back into Flask 1. This ensures complete mixing of the two solutions. Note the time of the color change from blue to yellow and record the time in seconds from initial mixing to final color change in your notebook. Repeat this process with the remaining pairs of flasks. If the values obtained for these three trials vary by more than 7 seconds, it would be wise to repeat this portion of the experiment and use the average of six trials (rather than three) in order to obtain as accurate a base rate as possible. Record the data in the Table.

NOTE: *Before beginning each new part of the experiment, the six Erlenmeyer flasks should be rinsed with acetone and drained well.*

Effects of Temperature

Prepare two water baths, one warmed carefully on a hot plate to approximately 10° above room temperature, and the second, cooled by the addition of ice, to approximately 10° below room temperature.* Repeat the standard technique, but allow the two flasks to equilibrate in the water bath for about five minutes before mixing the solutions. The mixture should also be kept in the bath until the color change has been timed. Maintaining constant temperature is critical to the success of this part of the experiment. Repeat each determination three times, and use the average of the three values to determine k at these two additional temperatures. Record the data in your Table.

Effect of Solvent

The above rate constants are for a solution that is 70% water and 30% acetone. In order to test the effect of solvent polarity, alter the standard procedure as follows:

This time, place only 2 mL of the 0.1 M solution of *t*-butyl chloride in acetone into Flask 1. Now, place just 0.2 mL of the sodium hydroxide solution, 7.8 mL of water, and the bromophenol blue indicator into Flask 2. Mix as in the standard technique method, and determine the time required for the color change in this 80% water-20% acetone solution. Do three trials as usual, and use the average to determine k. Record all data in your Table.

Calculations

1. Compare the average value of k at the three different temperatures. Recall the rule of thumb that by "changing the temperature by ten degrees, the rate is doubled/halved." Is that what you observed?

2. a. What effect was observed on increasing the water from 70 to 80% of the solvent mixture?

   b. Does the acetone participate directly in the reaction? What is the function of the acetone?

   c. Does the water participate directly in the reaction?

   d. What effect would you predict if the solvent were 60% water:40% acetone?

---

* It is not necessary to obtain exactly a 10° change in the temperature, but record the actual temperature used and keep it as constant as possible during the determination.

3. The mathematical equation for the activation energy of a reaction was developed by S. Arrhenius, and it is as follows:

$$k = Ae^{-\frac{E_a}{RT}}$$

where k = rate constant, A is a constant, E_a is the activation energy, R = gas constant $\left(1.99\dfrac{cal}{mole\ K}\right)$, and T is the temperature in °K.

The above equation can be simplified into logarithmic form to:

$$\log k = \left(\frac{-E_a}{2.30R} \cdot \frac{1}{T}\right) + \log A$$

This is actually the equation of a straight line (y = mx + b) where y = log k, b = log A (*i.e.*, the y-intercept), x = 1/T, and $m = \dfrac{-E_a}{2.30R}$ (the slope of the line.)

Therefore, a plot of –log k (on the y-axis) versus $\dfrac{1}{T}$ (on the x-axis, the reciprocal of the absolute temperature) should be a straight line whose slope is equal to $\dfrac{E_a}{2.30R}$. Plot your values *on graph paper*, and determine the approximate value for E_a with its appropriate units.

CHAPTER 11

The Grignard Reaction—
Preparation of Benzoic Acid

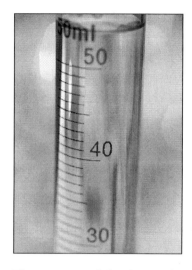

INTRODUCTION

When a solution of alkyl or aryl halide in dry diethyl ether is allowed to stand over metallic magnesium turnings, a vigorous reaction takes place. The solution initially turns cloudy, begins to boil, and the magnesium gradually disappears. The result is the formation of a gray-black solution known as a Grignard reagent. This reagent, discovered by the French chemist Victor Grignard of the University of Lyons in 1898, earned him the Nobel Prize in 1912. Since its discovery, this reagent has become one of the most useful and versatile synthetic reagents available to the organic chemist.

The structure of the Grignard reagent is usually written as RMgX or R–MgX, and the equation for its formation is written as follows:

$$R-X \quad + \quad Mg \quad \xrightarrow[\text{ether}]{\text{dry}} \quad R-Mg-X$$

[where R is either an alkyl or aryl group and X is Cl, Br, or I]

Once formed, the reagent reacts easily with a variety of compounds including aldehydes, ketones, esters, carbon dioxide, and nitriles to yield a variety of products. The value of the reagent can be seen in the fact that when Grignard died in 1935, over 6,000 scientific papers dealing with the subject had already been published.

A few of the more common reactions of Grignard reagents are given below:

PREPARATION OF :

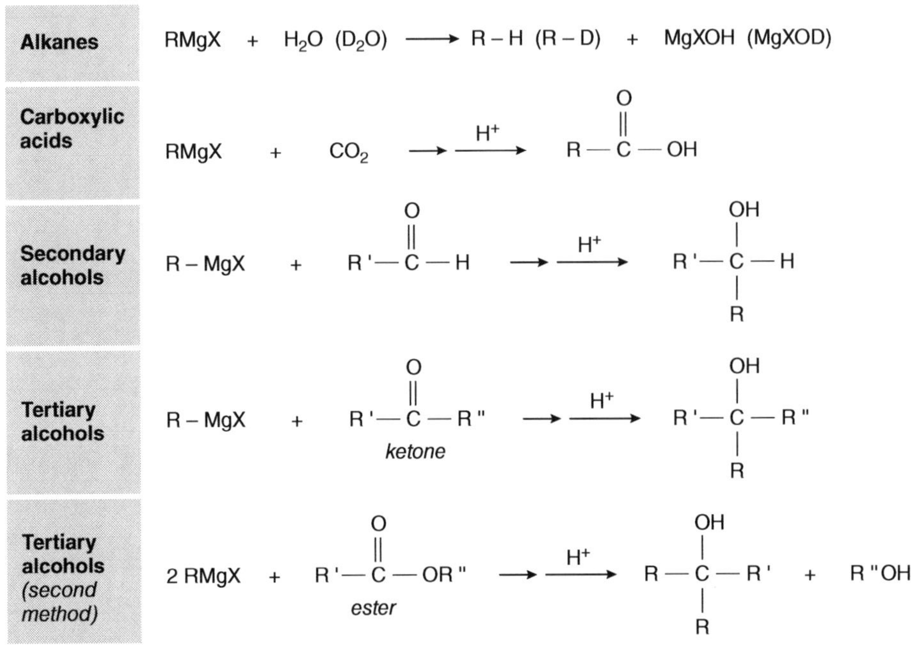

Alkanes	$RMgX$ + H_2O (D_2O) ⟶ $R-H$ $(R-D)$ + $MgXOH$ $(MgXOD)$
Carboxylic acids	$RMgX$ + CO_2 ⟶ $\xrightarrow{H^+}$ $R-\overset{\displaystyle O}{\overset{\|}{C}}-OH$
Secondary alcohols	$R-MgX$ + $R'-\overset{\displaystyle O}{\overset{\|}{C}}-H$ ⟶ $\xrightarrow{H^+}$ $R'-\overset{\displaystyle OH}{\underset{\displaystyle R}{\overset{\|}{C}}}-H$
Tertiary alcohols	$R-MgX$ + $R'-\overset{\displaystyle O}{\overset{\|}{C}}-R''$ (ketone) ⟶ $\xrightarrow{H^+}$ $R'-\overset{\displaystyle OH}{\underset{\displaystyle R}{\overset{\|}{C}}}-R''$
Tertiary alcohols (second method)	$2\,RMgX$ + $R'-\overset{\displaystyle O}{\overset{\|}{C}}-OR''$ (ester) ⟶ $\xrightarrow{H^+}$ $R-\overset{\displaystyle OH}{\underset{\displaystyle R}{\overset{\|}{C}}}-R'$ + $R''OH$

In addition to the preparation of the various functional groups shown above, the Grignard reagent also has great utility in the synthesis of other organometallic compounds. For example:

$$RMgX \quad + \quad HgCl_2 \quad \longrightarrow \quad RHgCl \quad + \quad MgXCl$$

$$3\,RMgX \quad + \quad SbCl_2 \quad \longrightarrow \quad R_3Sb \quad + \quad 3\,MgXCl$$

$$2\,RMgX \quad + \quad R'_2SnCl_2 \quad \longrightarrow \quad R_2SnR'_2 \quad + \quad 2\,MgXCl$$

The alkyl portion of the Grignard reagent has the characteristics of a **carbanion**. That is, the bond-forming process involving an R – MgX molecule may be thought of as proceeding via an $R{:}^{\ominus}$ species.

The Grignard reagent functions as a good nucleophile in nucleophilic addition reactions to the carbonyl group. The carbonyl group is electrophilic at the carbon atom, and a good nucleophile will seek out this center for addition.

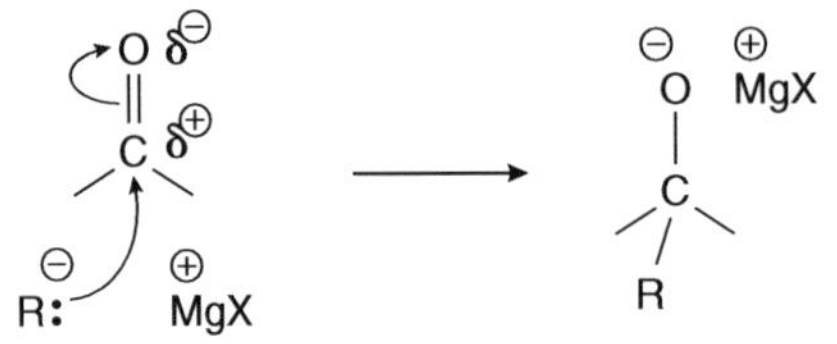

Because the Grignard reagent reacts with water, carbon dioxide, and oxygen, it must be protected from air and moisture when it is used. The apparatus in which the reaction is to be conducted must be scrupulously dry, and the solvent must be free of water (anhydrous) as well. During the reaction, the contents of the flask must be protected from atmospheric moisture by a calcium chloride drying tube. Oxygen should also be excluded. This can be done by allowing the solvent (ether) to reflux. The resulting blanket of solvent vapor keeps air from the surface of the reaction mixture.

The Grignard synthesis that will be carried out in this experiment is:

In this experiment, the principal by-product is **biphenyl**, which is formed by a heat- or light-catalyzed coupling reaction of the Grignard reagent with unreacted bromobenzene. Too high a reaction temperature favors the formation of this product.

Since Grignard reactions can frequently be difficult to start, all glassware should be oven-dried overnight, and the entire apparatus should be flamed *before* starting the reaction. The Grignard reagent cannot be stored; it must be used as soon as it is prepared.

Procedure

Part A: Preparation of the Grignard Reagent—Phenylmagnesium Bromide

All glassware to be used must be thoroughly *dry* (oven-dried, if possible) before beginning the preparation of the Grignard reagent.

Set up the apparatus for the reaction as shown in Figure 11-1: a 250 mL, 3-neck, round-bottom flask with a reflux condenser (plus $CaCl_2$ drying tube) in the center neck, an addition funnel (plus drying tube) in the right neck, and a ground glass stopper in the left neck. The apparatus should be about 6 inches from the base of the ring stand and *securely clamped* at the center neck. The $CaCl_2$ in the drying tubes should be anhydrous, and the glass wool plugs should be sufficient to support the $CaCl_2$, but not so thick as to preclude vapors from escaping.

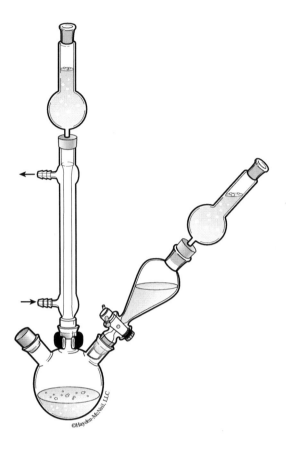

Figure 11-1. *Apparatus for the Grignard Reaction.*

Weigh about 1 g of magnesium turnings, and record the exact amount in your notebook. Add the magnesium to the round-bottom flask.

In the hood, measure about 5 mL of bromobenzene, and mix it well with about 25 mL of dry ether. Pour the bromobenzene/ether mixture into the separatory funnel that is already connected to your apparatus (be sure the stopcock is closed).

Obtain a metal pan, and fill it with hot water from the faucet. Allow water to flow through the condenser, and add enough of the bromobenzene/ether mixture to the round-bottom flask in order to just cover the magnesium. **Be careful that your hoses are connected well and that no water should be leaking into your reaction vessel (this will cause alkane formation).** Place the pan of hot water under the round-bottom flask, and shake occasionally until reaction starts. Evidence for reaction consists of one or more of the following: bubbles forming on the magnesium, a cloudy gray or brownish look to the ether, or heat evolution which causes the ether to reflux. If heating and shaking do not initiate the reaction, ask your instructor for help. Once the Grignard reagent has begun to form, the exothermic nature of the reaction will be obvious. This reaction can become quite vigorous, and it is therefore wise to have a pan of cold water available should the reflux rate become excessive. However, once the reaction has begun, it should be continued by adding the rest of the bromobenzene/ether solution at a rate of about 1–2 drops per second in order to maintain a gentle reflux.

When all of the bromobenzene/ether solution has been added and almost all of the magnesium has reacted, reflux the mixture with occasional stirring or shaking for an additional 10–15 minutes using a warm water bath. Once the phenylmagnesium bromide (or any Grignard reagent, for that matter) has been prepared, it must be used immediately in the next step.

REMEMBER: *Ether boils at 35°C.*

Part B: Preparation of Benzoic Acid

Once the phenylmagnesium bromide in ether has been prepared, proceed as follows:

Crush about 25 g of dry ice (CO_2) in a paper towel, and weigh out 20 g into a dry, 250 mL beaker. *In the hood,* pour the Grignard reagent (the phenylmagnesium bromide solution) over the dry ice while stirring with a glass rod. Keep the unreacted magnesium inside the round-bottom flask. Note that the reaction is *extremely vigorous,* and the mixture becomes a stiff paste. This step should be done in the hood to prevent ether fumes from filling the laboratory. Continue to stir the mixture until all of the CO_2(excess) has evolved.

While still in the hood, *carefully* add 25–30 mL of hot water (80°C) *in small portions* to evaporate the ether. If the water is added all at once, the ether may boil over. If ether still remains, carefully warm the reaction mixture in a 50°C water bath (NO FLAMES) **in the hood.** The residue should be white and oatmeal-like in texture. Add 6 M HCl (slowly!) to the mixture until it is acidic (pH 2–3). Be very careful, since the addition of too much HCl may dissolve the benzoic acid. Make sure to use blue litmus paper to measure pH.

NOTE: *Reaction with the HCl is also quite exothermic and produces hydrogen gas. If any residual ether were present, it would boil off, possibly vigorously.*

Chill the mixture in an ice bath, and collect the product (crude benzoic acid plus biphenyl by-product) by vacuum filtration. Let the impure product dry before weighing and finding the melting point.

This is a good point to stop the procedure if necessary.

At this point, the benzoic acid (m.p. 120–122°C) is contaminated by varying amounts of biphenyl (m.p. 69–71°C).

An efficient method for separating the two products is extraction. Mix the product with about 15 mL of 10% $NaHCO_3$ solution, and check the solution with pH paper to be sure that it is basic. Use additional $NaHCO_3$ solution if necessary to make the solution basic. Extract the mixture (successively) with several portions of diethyl ether to remove the biphenyl. Two 10 mL portions of ether should be sufficient. Combine the ether extracts, and dry over anhydrous sodium sulfate. While the ether is drying, acidify the basic, aqueous solution of sodium benzoate by the dropwise addition of 6 M HCl until a pH of 2–3 is obtained. The precipitated benzoic acid can be isolated by vacuum filtration, washed with ice-cold water, and dried. The biphenyl can be isolated by filtering off the drying agent and evaporating the ether (do this in the hood) using a hot water bath. In this way both the major and minor products are obtained.

Record the weight and melting point of each product, and calculate the percent yield of each.

CHAPTER 12

Fischer Esterification

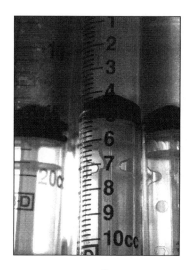

INTRODUCTION

Esters are very common compounds; we consume and use them every day. Esters are important components of foods, drugs, solvents, and fabrics. Many of the compounds found in flavors (especially fruit flavors) are esters.

One of the simplest and oldest known organic reactions is the condensation of a carboxylic acid and an alcohol to form an ester.

This reaction is called the Fischer esterification in honor of Emil Fischer, a famous German chemist of the late nineteenth and early twentieth centuries who won the Nobel Prize in chemistry for determining the structure of glucose. The reaction is catalyzed by strong acid and takes place by the following mechanism:

In this experiment, a Fischer esterification will be carried out using acetic acid and isoamyl alcohol to produce isoamyl acetate, an ester that smells like bananas when concentrated and like pears when in dilute aqueous solution.

Acetic acid
b.p. 118°C

Isoamyl alcohol
b.p. 130°C

Isoamyl acetate
b.p. 142°C

Procedure

> **NOTE:** *There are three steps to this procedure: a 1-hour reflux, two washings, and a simple distillation. To complete this procedure in 3 hours, it is important to be well organized and to plan ahead.*

In a 50 mL round-bottom flask in the fume hood, place 50 mmol of isoamyl alcohol and 100 mmol of acetic acid. Cautiously add 20 drops of concentrated sulfuric acid. Add boiling chips, a condenser, heating mantle, and variable transformer, establish a low, constant water flow through the condenser, and heat the mixture at reflux for one hour. At the end of the reflux period, cool the flask in an ice bath, and pour the contents into a small separatory funnel. Wash the reaction mixture with one 20 mL portion of water, and then with one 20 mL portion of 5% aqueous sodium bicarbonate solution. After adding the bicarbonate, stir the layers together. Do not stopper the separatory funnel until gas evolution has ceased (the bicarbonate is neutralizing any residual acetic acid or sulfuric acid present). *Vent the separatory funnel often while shaking to avoid pressure buildup.* As with all extractions, pay attention to which layer is which, and save all washings until you are sure where your product is.

Dry the crude ester with anhydrous $MgSO_4$ for five minutes, then filter it through fluted filter paper into a clean, dry 50 mL round-bottom flask. Set up for simple distillation, and collect the fraction boiling above 120°C (while the boiling point of isoamyl acetate is reported to be 142°C, commercial grade material may boil over a range of 120–145°). Weigh the product, and calculate the percent yield.

Run an infrared spectrum on your product (as a neat liquid). See the "Eugenol from Cloves Experiment" for instructions on taking an IR spectrum.

CHAPTER 13

Saponification of Fat—
The Preparation of Soap from Shortening

The making of soap is one of the oldest synthetic organic reactions known, ranking second only to the production of ethyl alcohol. Credit for its manufacture is usually given to the ancient Phoenicians, who, around 600 BC, prepared it from goats' tallow and wood ashes.

The manufacture of soap involves the alkaline hydrolysis (also referred to as saponification) of a fat or oil to yield soap plus glycerol. Fat consists of a mixture of organic molecules called triglycerides which are esters of long-chain fatty acids, usually containing from 12 to 18 carbon atoms in a straight chain. They may be fully saturated or unsaturated (containing one or more C=C double bonds). If they are unsaturated, the *cis*-isomer of the double bond is found predominantly. Examples are given below. The esters of olive oil, for example, contain about 64% oleic acid, 16% linoleic acid, and 14% palmitic acid as primary constituents. Soap consists of a mixture of the sodium or potassium salts of the long-chain carboxylic acids and is formed when hydroxide ion cleaves the triglyceride.

Coconut Oil	Lauric acid [$CH_3(CH_2)_{10}COOH$] Myristic acid [$CH_3(CH_2)_{12}COOH$]
Olive Oil	Palmitic acid [$CH_3(CH_2)_{14}COOH$] Oleic acid [cis–$CH_3(CH_2)_7CH=CH(CH_2)_7COOH$] Linoleic acid [$cis,cis$–$CH_3(CH_2)_4CH=CHCH_2CH=CH(CH_2)_7COOH$]
Tallow	Palmitic, Oleic, and Stearic acid [$CH_3(CH_2)_{16}COOH$]

Triglyceride   Soap   Glycerol
(fat or oil)

A particular fat or oil generally has at least two different fatty acids incorporated into its ester structure; *i.e.*, R, R′, and R″ are usually different groups within the same tri-acylglycerol molecule. The general percentage of each fatty acid within a given fat or oil is characteristic to that fat or oil (see above).

Much attention is given today to the role of oils and fats in nutrition and disease. For example, linoleic acid cannot be biosynthesized and must be obtained via the diet. Similarly, unsaturated acids are thought to be involved in the biosynthesis of prosta-glandins. The latter help control blood pressure and muscle contraction, are important in the functioning of biological membranes, and have been implicated in the preven-tion or occurrence of diseases such as cancer, multiple sclerosis, and atherosclerosis. Polyunsaturated fatty acids, especially those with C=C double bonds located at the third and sixth carbon atoms from the terminal methyl group, seem to be particularly effective in hastening the excretion or breakdown of cholesterol, thus preventing its arterial accumulation and vascular disease. Saturated fats work in the opposite way. Monounsaturated fatty acids are neutral in their benefit/harm ratio; however, some polyunsaturated fatty acids are actually tumor promoters.

Oils have lower melting points than fats, generally because of the presence of more sites of unsaturation. The formation of an orderly crystalline structure is impeded by the pres-ence of *cis*-substituted double bonds. If, however, oils are partially hydrogenated with hydrogen and a metal catalyst, a semisolid fat such as Crisco is obtained. The saturated chains fit more easily into a crystal structure and therefore possess higher melting points.

The sodium or potassium salts of the fatty acids derived from the saponification of fats and oils are used as soaps. The chief animal fats used in this process are lard (from hogs) and tallow (from sheep or cattle); the main oils used are coconut, palm, and olive. The specific R-groups present in a soap give it characteristic properties. For example, shorter chain length R-groups will increase the water-solubility of the soap.

Tallow, obtained by melting cattle fat with steam, is the chief fatty material used in soap making. Before the saponification process is begun, coconut oil is usually added to pro-duce a softer, more water-soluble soap (since its saponification products are lauric and myristic acids that contain small, saturated hydrocarbon chains). Saponification of tallow produces mainly the salts of palmitic, stearic, and oleic acids, longer in chain length than those from coconut oil. Lard contains somewhat greater amounts of oleic acid.

Saponification of pure coconut oil yields a very water-soluble soap. It lathers even in sea water. Remember this the next time your soap "melts" away in the soap dish. Most toilet soaps are obtained from palm oil, which yields predominantly oleic and palmitic acids upon saponification. Olive oil (which will be used in this experiment) yields mainly oleic acid. It is used to prepare Castile soap (named after a region in Spain where olive oil originated).

In preparing usable soaps, the excess alkali (NaOH, KOH) used in the process must be removed as it is harmful to skin. It is advantageous to leave some glycerol behind, as it lubricates and softens skin. Perfumes and medicinal agents may also be added. Floating soap (Ivory) is prepared by blowing air into the saponified melt as it solidifies. Using KOH instead of NaOH during saponification produces the softer soaps used in shaving creams and liquid soaps, while fine sand, sodium carbonate, or pumice are added as abrasives and are sold as scouring soaps.

A soap molecule has a polar, water-soluble head, $-COO^-$, and a long, nonpolar, oil-soluble tail, the long chain of the remaining carbon atoms. Ordinarily, oil and water tend to separate, forming two distinct layers, but the presence of soap changes this. The long nonpolar ends of the soap molecules dissolve in the oil droplets, leaving the polar, water-soluble ends projecting outward into the surrounding water. Each individual droplet thus becomes surrounded by negative charges. Repulsion between these charges keeps the oil droplets from coalescing, and a stable emulsion of oil in water forms. Since the oil is what holds the dirt, emulsifying or "cutting" the oil also **emulsifies** or "frees" the dirt and allows it to be washed away with the rinse water.

Soap, however, has the disadvantage of being a less effective cleaner in hard water, due to the presence of calcium, magnesium, and iron salts that react with soap to yield insoluble precipitates frequently called soap curd or soap scum. This precipitate is actually the calcium, magnesium, or iron salts of the long-chain fatty acids. This problem can be lessened for laundry soaps through the addition of a water softener, such as sodium carbonate, that precipitates the hard water ions.

Hard water is not a problem, however, with detergents, which is one reason why detergents have replaced soap for many household uses. Synthetic detergents are structurally similar to soaps, except that the carboxylate ions [$-COO^-$] at the end of the hydrocarbon chains are replaced with sulfonate [$-SO_3^-$] or sulfate [$-OSO_3^-$] ions:

$$CH_3(CH_2)_nCH_2SO_2O^-Na^+ \text{ (an alkanesulfonate) or}$$

$$CH_3(CH_2)_nCH_2OSO_2O^-Na^+ \text{ (an alkyl sulfate)}$$

The calcium, magnesium, and iron salts of these long-chain sulfonates and sulfates do not precipitate from water. This results in greater cleaning effectiveness in hard water without the need for water-softening agents. The main disadvantage to detergents is that they are generally nonbiodegradable.

In this experiment, you will prepare soap by the alkaline hydrolysis or saponification of a fat or oil which is, remember, an ester.

Procedure

Making the Soap

Place 10 mL of deionized water and 10 mL of 95% ethanol into a 100 mL round-bottom flask, and dissolve 3 gm of sodium hydroxide pellets (the solution will get hot). Add 3 gm of a commercial oil or solid shortening and a few boiling chips. Then attach a reflux condenser, and reflux the mixture for at least 45 minutes.

In the meantime, prepare a solution of 15 g of sodium chloride in 50 mL of water in a 100 mL beaker. *Do not use table salt*, due to the presence of other components. Heat the solution if necessary to dissolve the salt, but allow it to cool to room temperature before using. To this salt solution, add the hot, refluxed mixture with stirring and cool to room temperature in an ice bath. Collect the precipitated soap by suction filtration and wash twice with small quantities of ice-cold water. Use part of the soap for the tests below, dry the remainder, and submit it in a properly labeled container to your instructor.

Tests On Soaps

1. *Residual Alkalinity*

    If soap contains residual alkali, it may be harmful to the skin or to clothing. To test for residual base, dissolve a small pellet of your soap in 5 mL of ethanol and add two drops of phenolphthalein. Record and explain your observations.

2. *Effect of Calcium and Magnesium Salts on Soaps and Detergents*

    Dissolve 0.35 g of your prepared soap in 25 mL of distilled water and place 5 mL of the solution in a test tube. Shake the solution to build a foam, allow the solution to stand for 30 seconds, observe the level of the foam, and record the result in your notebook. Add 3 drops of 5% calcium chloride solution, shake, and allow to stand. Observe the effect of the calcium chloride on the foam and record the result. Did you notice anything? Add 0.3 g of trisodium phosphate or sodium carbonate and shake again. Allow the solution to stand, and note and record the result.

    Repeat the above tests with a second 5 mL portion of fresh soap solution, using 5% magnesium chloride solution. Note and record all the results.

Dissolve 0.35 g of a *commercial detergent* in 25 mL of distilled water and place 5 mL of the solution in a test tube. Shake the solution to build a foam, allow the solution to stand for 30 seconds, observe the effect of the calcium chloride on the foam and record the result. Did you notice anything? Is there a need for trisodium phosphate or sodium carbonate? Why?

Repeat the above tests with a second 5 mL portion of fresh detergent solution, using 5% magnesium chloride solution. Note and record all the results.

3.   *Effect of Oil*

Place 5 drops of a vegetable oil into each of three test tubes. To the first add 5 mL of distilled water, to the second add 5 mL of fresh soap solution, and to the third add 5 mL of fresh detergent solution. Shake each tube vigorously, let stand a few minutes, and compare and record the results.

4.   *Effect of Dilute Acid*

To the remaining 10 mL of soap solution and 10 mL of detergent solution, add dilute sulfuric acid until the solutions are acidic (pH 1). Note and record the result in each case.

Questions

1.   Why does dissolving soap in water produce an alkaline solution?

2.   Why is a mixture of alcohol and water used, rather than simply water itself, to saponify the fat or oil to produce soap?

3.   Why is it impossible to calculate an exact theoretical yield of soap?

4.   Explain the results of adding calcium and magnesium salts to a solution of your prepared soap. Explain what happened after the trisodium phosphate or sodium carbonate was added.

5.   Explain the results of adding dilute sulfuric acid to your soap and detergent solutions.

CHM **2211L**

Organic Chemistry II
Laboratory Manual

CHAPTER 14

Review of Recrystallization—
The Isolation of Acetylsalicylic Acid
from Aspirin Tablets

Last semester in Organic Chemistry Lab I, you learned how to purify an impure solid by recrystallization. Since this is a very important technique and students usually have a lot trouble with it, we will start this semester with a review of this technique.

There are some very important points to remember when you are performing a recrystallization. Remember that recrystallization is a method of purification. The exact procedure that one uses depends on how impure the compound is. First, you must find a solvent that will dissolve the solid when hot, but not dissolve the solid when cold. This is because crystallization should occur when the solution is cooled. If the solution is only slightly colored, impurities will remain dissolved in the solvent and will not be a problem. Otherwise, activated charcoal may be needed. Fluted filter paper is needed for the hot filtration. Fluting allows for a greater surface area of filter paper to come into contact with the filtrate. This allows filtration to occur faster—before the solution has time to cool. Vacuum filtration into a Büchner funnel is always used to collect and dry the crystals.

The general steps for any recrystallization are as follows:

1. Select a proper solvent.

2. Heat the solvent to its boiling point.

3. Dissolve the solid compound in the *minimum amount* of boiling solvent.

4. Add decolorizing charcoal if necessary.

5. Filter the hot mixture through a heated, wide-stem or stemless funnel to remove any insoluble impurities (or the decolorizing charcoal, if you used it).

6. Allow the hot solution to cool *slowly* to room temperature or lower.

7. If crystals do not appear, scratch the solution against the flask with a glass rod, cool the solution further, or add a seed crystal of saved product.

8. Collect the crystals by suction filtration, using a Büchner funnel.

9. Rinse the crystals with a *small amount* of *cold* solvent.

10. If worthwhile, obtain a second crop of crystals.

Experimental Procedure

Weigh out 5 aspirin tablets into a 125 mL Erlenmeyer flask. Warm a small amount of toluene (record the approximate volume used) using a boiling water bath in a metal pan on a hot plate. Dissolve the aspirin tablets in a minimum amount of hot toluene. You may need to crush the tablets at this point to speed up solution. If any insoluble solid material remains, do not try to dissolve it by adding more toluene. Remove the insoluble material by filtering the *hot* solution through fluted filter paper into a small Erlenmeyer flask. Rinse the filter paper and the funnel with a few mLs of hot toluene.

> **NOTE:** *Use a stemless or short-stem funnel for the hot filtration. (Why?) Make sure that the funnel and its Erlenmeyer flask are kept* hot *during the filtration. This can be done by keeping them on a hot plate throughout the filtration procedure with a small amount of boiling toluene constantly refluxing in the flask.*
>
> *If you do not remember how to flute filter paper, ask your instructor for a demonstration.*
>
> *The most important thing to remember at this point of the procedure is to **keep things hot**.*

Cool the filtrate to room temperature, and then place the flask in an ice/water bath until the aspirin crystallizes. If the purified aspirin does not crystallize, use a glass rod to scratch the sides of the flask while the solution is kept in the ice/water bath. If this does not work, add a *small* amount of hexane and stir while adding. Collect the recrystallized aspirin on a Büchner funnel using vacuum filtration. Wash the aspirin with small amounts of ice-cold hexane to remove traces of toluene.

Let the crystals air dry before weighing them and determining the melting point range.

Calculate the percent recovery of acetylsalicylic acid from the aspirin tablets.

CHAPTER 15

Oxidation of an Aromatic Side Chain—
Identification of an Unknown Chlorotoluene

Alkylbenzenes undergo oxidation with the aliphatic side chain being converted to a carboxylic acid which is directly attached to the aromatic ring. Thus methyl-, ethyl-, propyl-, and butylbenzenes upon oxidation will all give benzoic acid.

$$
\underset{\text{Cl}}{\overset{\text{CH}_3}{\bigcirc}} \xrightarrow[\Delta]{\text{KMnO}_4} \underset{\text{Cl}}{\overset{\text{COOH}}{\bigcirc}} + \text{MnO}_2
$$

The three isomeric chlorotoluenes have similar physical properties, and they are difficult to distinguish by most instrumental methods. If, however, they are converted by oxidation to their respective chlorobenzoic acids, their properties are no longer similar, and they are easily differentiated. In this experiment, each student will identify an unknown chlorotoluene by converting it to the corresponding benzoic acid and determining its melting point.

	b.p.		m.p.
2-chlorotoluene	157–159°C	2-chlorobenzoic acid	138–140°C
3-chlorotoluene	160–162°C	3-chlorobenzoic acid	155–157°C
4-chlorotoluene	162–164°C	4-chlorobenzoic acid	239–241°C

Refluxing

In order to achieve a successful reaction, it is often necessary to use a reflux apparatus. The word reflux means "to return" which is exactly what the process entails. The principle behind the process is that a reaction is run at a constant temperature at or near a solvent's boiling points. A condenser (either cooled by water or air) will condense the vapors produced through the boiling of solvent and return it to the reaction vessel. The reflux condenser can either be water-cooled or air-cooled.

Experimental Procedure

1. Obtain a sample of an unknown chlorotoluene from your instructor. Record the number of your unknown in your lab notebook.

2. Place 50 mL of water, 3.0 g of potassium permanganate, and 1 mL of the chlorotoluene in a 250 mL round-bottom flask. Add 2–3 pellets of sodium hydroxide to the flask. Add boiling chips following the addition of the sodium hydroxide. Retain a few drops of your unknown for possible use later.

3. Assemble a simple reflux apparatus. Use a heating mantle as the heat source.

4. Reflux at high temperature until the purple color has gone, or for one hour. Stop heating at this point, and allow the mixture to cool slightly. Remove the condenser and test for permanganate.

    NOTE: To see if all of the permanganate has reacted, place a drop of the reaction mixture on a piece of filter paper. If the brown spot on the paper is surrounded by a purple ring, permanganate is still present, and heating should be continued.

5. If after one hour the permanganate is still present, add small amounts of 30% sodium bisulfite solution* until the purple color is gone. (Test the reaction mixture after each addition of bisulfite using the method described above.)

    ***NOTE TO INSTRUCTOR:** The sodium bisulfite solution should be relatively fresh (no more than one week old).*

6. While still hot, filter the mixture through Whatman filter paper #42. Discard the used filter cake in the solid waste container labeled for chemical disposal.

7. Very carefully add 5 mL of concentrated hydrochloric acid to the filtrate, with stirring. A voluminous white precipitate of the chlorobenzoic acid will form.

8. Allow the solution to cool for a few minutes. Finally, use an ice/water bath to complete the crystallization process.

    The product is quite pure and needs no recrystallization.

9. Vacuum filter the product. Wash the precipitate with cold water. Dry your product by pressing the solid between two pieces of filter paper.

    NOTE: An oven set to 100°C may be used to speed drying. The aqueous layer may be flushed down the drain.

10. Using the m.p. of your chlorobenzoic acid as a guide, determine which unknown chlorotoluene you had. Turn in your yield along with the identification of your unknown to your instructor.

Questions

1. What substance produces the brown/black spot on the filter paper in step 4?

2. Assume that your product has a m.p. of 187–190°C. Even though this value does not match any of the isomers, you could still reasonably state which chlorotoluene you started with. Explain.

3. In what form is the product (the chlorobenzoic acid) in the clear filtrate after the brown precipitate has been removed? After the addition of the hydrochloric acid?

4. What happens to the pH of the reaction mixture as the oxidation reaction proceeds?

5. Explain the use of the filter paper in this experiment. Also explain what the #42 indicates about the paper's properties.

6. Why do you use an ice/water mixture in step 8 for an ice bath rather than pure ice?

CHAPTER 16

**Organic Synthesis—
The Last Two Steps in a Multi-step Synthesis
of Methyl *m*-Nitrobenzoate**

INTRODUCTION

Thus far, the organic procedures you have encountered in the laboratory have involved the synthesis of organic molecules through simple, one-step transformations. In reality, most desired molecules cannot be made from readily available starting materials in just one step. A multi-step reaction scheme (referred to as a **synthesis**) is required.

As an example of a multi-step synthesis, you will be doing some aromatic chemistry by preparing methyl *m*-nitrobenzoate.

COOCH$_3$

NO$_2$

Methyl
m-Nitrobenzoate

In designing a synthetic scheme, the structure of the final product is compared with that of a readily available (and inexpensive) starting molecule. In designing this particular synthesis, benzene is used as the starting material. The chemist would consider several factors:

1. Two substituents must be placed on the aromatic ring (the nitro group and the carboxylate group).

2. A nitro group can be directly substituted onto an aromatic ring by electrophilic aromatic substitution.

3. A carboxylate group cannot be directly substituted onto an aromatic ring. The ester must therefore be prepared by esterification of the corresponding carboxylic acid. A carboxylic acid function can also not be directly substituted onto an aromatic ring and must be made by transformation of some other substituent.

4. Oxidation of the aliphatic side chain of an alkylbenzene will transform the alkyl group into a carboxyl group. The alkyl group can be directly substituted onto the aromatic ring by Friedel-Crafts alkylation.

5. The final consideration is the effect of the presence of a substituent already present on an aromatic ring on the addition of a second substituent to that ring. While an alkyl group is an *ortho, para* director, a carboxylate group is a *meta* director.

Putting all of these factors together would lead the organic chemist to the following four-step synthetic sequence for the preparation of methyl *m*-nitrobenzoate from benzene:

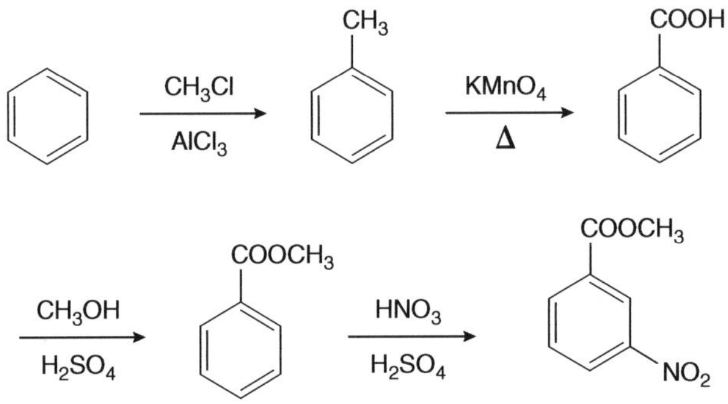

In this experiment you will be performing the last two steps of this synthetic sequence, a Fischer esterification followed by a nitration (electrophilic aromatic substitution).

FISCHER ESTERIFICATION OF BENZOIC ACID

One of the simplest and oldest known organic reactions is the reaction of a carboxylic acid and an alcohol to form an ester. This reaction is called the Fischer esterification in honor of Emil Fischer, a German chemist of the late nineteenth and early twentieth centuries, who won the Nobel Prize in chemistry for determining the structure of glucose.

The Fischer esterification is catalyzed by strong acids, and occurs by the following mechanism:

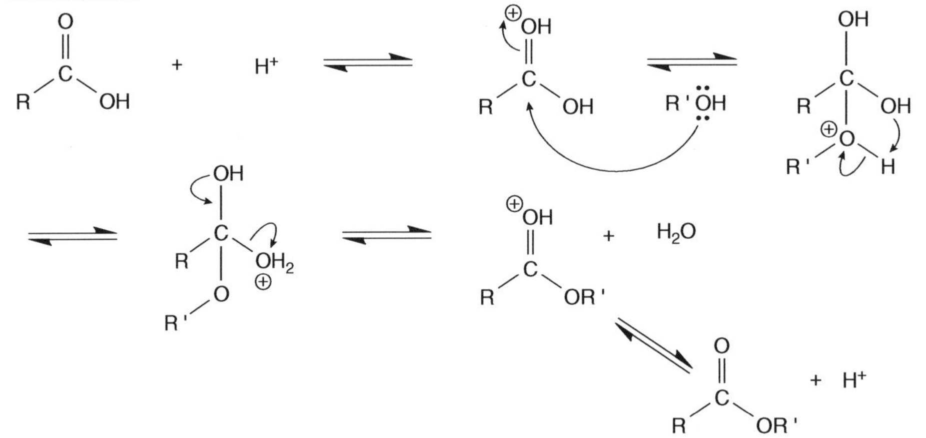

Your first step in this synthesis will be the Fischer esterification of benzoic acid with methyl alcohol to produce methyl benzoate.

O═C—OH (Benzoic Acid) + CH₃OH →[H⁺] O═C—OCH₃ (Methyl benzoate) + H₂O

Benzoic Acid
m.p. 122°C

Methyl alcohol
b.p. 65°C

Methyl benzoate
b.p. 198°C

Procedure

Place 10.0 g of benzoic acid and 25 mL of methanol in a 100 mL round-bottom flask, and cool the mixture in an ice bath. *Carefully* dispense 3 mL of concentrated sulfuric acid by automatic dispenser into a small (25 mL or 50 mL) Erlenmeyer flask. *Carefully pour this sulfuric acid from the Erlenmeyer flask into the round-bottom flask*—pouring it slowly down the walls so that it cools before it enters the solution. Then swirl the flask to mix the components. (Perform this operation in the hood in order to avoid carrying concentrated sulfuric acid around the lab.)

Attach a reflux condenser to the flask, add a boiling chip, and—using a heating mantle with Variac as the heat source—reflux the mixture gently for one hour.

Cool the solution, decant into a separatory funnel containing 50 mL of water, and rinse the flask with 35 mL of *t*-butyl methyl ether. Add this ether to the separatory funnel, shake thoroughly releasing pressure periodically, and drain off the water layer that contains the sulfuric acid and the bulk of the methanol. Wash the ether solution that remains in the separatory funnel with 25 mL of water followed by 25 mL of saturated aqueous sodium bicarbonate solution (to remove unreacted benzoic acid). Again shake, with frequent release of pressure, by inverting the separatory funnel and opening the stopcock until no further reaction is apparent. Then drain off the bicarbonate layer into a beaker. Wash the *t*-butyl methyl ether layer that is still in the separatory funnel with 15 mL of saturated sodium chloride solution, transfer the organic layer to an Erlenmeyer flask, and dry the ether solution over anhydrous calcium chloride. Add sufficient calcium chloride so that it no longer clumps together on the bottom of the flask. After 10 minutes, decant the dried ether solution into a round-bottom flask, wash the drying agent with an additional 3–5 mL of *t*-butyl methyl ether, and decant again.

Remove the ether by simple distillation (*t*-butyl methyl ether boils at 55°C).

When all of the *t*-butyl methyl ether has been distilled off, add 2 to 3 g of anhydrous calcium chloride pellets to the residual oil and heat for about 5 minutes longer. Then decant the methyl benzoate into a 50 mL round-bottom flask, and set up the necessary glassware for a **short-path distillation** (3-way adapter with thermometer adapter attached directly to the vacuum adapter—no condenser). Use a heating mantle as the heat source. If you do not have a 50 mL heating mantle and must use a larger, 100 mL mantle, use glass wool to fill the space between the mantle wall and the wall of the flask.

> **NOTE:** *Since the methyl benzoate is so high-boiling, a high setting on the variable transformer (70–80%) will be necessary.*

> **NOTE:** *The 3-way adapter should be insulated by either wrapping it—not too tightly—with several layers of aluminum foil or with some glass wool. This is done because a high boiling substance such as methyl benzoate will condense while going up the adapter, and it may be impossible to apply enough heat to drive the material over without adequate insulation.*

Use a tared 25 mL Erlenmeyer flask as the distillation receiver, and collect material boiling above 190°C. A typical student yield is about 7 g.

Cleanup

Pour the sulfuric acid layer into water, combine it with the bicarbonate layer, and flush the solution down the drain with much water. The saturated sodium chloride layer can also be flushed down the drain. If the calcium chloride is free of *t*-butyl methyl ether and methyl benzoate, it can be placed in the trash. Any remaining *t*-butyl methyl ether should be placed in the organic waste container along with any pot residues from the final distillation.

Questions

1. How many moles of benzoic acid did you use in this reaction? How many moles of methanol did you use? Why was this particular molar ratio of reactants chosen?

    HINT: *Remember the mechanism of the Fischer esterification.*

2. In the preparation of methyl benzoate, what is the purpose of (a) washing the organic layer with sodium bicarbonate solution? (b) washing the organic layer with saturated sodium chloride solution? (c) treating the organic layer with anhydrous calcium chloride pellets?

3. When extracting the ether solution with aqueous sodium bicarbonate solution, why were you cautioned to frequently invert the separatory funnel and open the stopcock?

4. Why was a condenser not necessary in the final distillation of the methyl benzoate?

MICROSCALE NITRATION OF METHYL BENZOATE

The nitration of methyl benzoate is a typical electrophilic aromatic substitution reaction. The electrophile is the nitronium ion (NO_2^+), which is formed by the reaction of nitric acid with sulfuric acid:

$$HNO_3 \; + \; 2\,H_2SO_4 \; \rightleftharpoons \; NO_2^{\oplus} \; + \; 2\,HSO_4^{\ominus} \; + \; H_3O^{\oplus}$$

The carboxylate group of the methyl benzoate, which is protonated by the solvent (sulfuric acid), is a *meta* director, because the nitronium ion (the electrophile) reacts at the ring carbon where the electron density is highest; *i.e.*, at a site where there is no positive charge in the resonance hybrid.

Procedure

CAUTION: *Be extremely careful when using concentrated sulfuric and concentrated nitric acids!*

Do this reaction in the fume hood.

Wipe up spills immediately and carefully using lots of water.

Using a Pasteur pipet, add 0.6 mL of concentrated sulfuric acid into a 10×100 mm test tube. Cool to 0°C and then add 0.30 g of methyl benzoate and cool again to 0 to 10°C.

In a second 10×100 mm text tube, prepare a sulfuric acid/nitric acid mixture by adding 0.2 mL of concentrated sulfuric acid into the test tube, cooling in an ice bath, and then carefully adding 0.2 mL of concentrated nitric acid into the same tube. Swirl to mix, and cool this mixture to 0 to 10°C. Now add *dropwise*, using a glass Pasteur pipet, the cooled sulfuric/nitric acid mixture to the cold methyl benzoate/sulfuric acid solution. During the addition of the acids, swirl the mixture frequently, and maintain the temperature of the reaction mixture in the range of 5 to 15°C.

When all of the nitric/sulfuric acid mixture has been added, allow the reaction mixture to warm to room temperature. After 15 minutes at room temperature, pour it onto 2.5 g of cracked ice in a small beaker. Stir.

Isolate the solid product by suction filtration using a small Hirsch funnel and a 25 mL filter flask, and wash well with water.

A small sample of this impure product should be saved and air-dried for later melting point and TLC analysis. The remainder is weighed and recrystallized in methanol.

The crude product should be obtained in about 80% yield and have a melting point of 74–76°C. The recrystallized product should have a melting point of 78°C.

Cleanup

Dilute the filtrate from the reaction with water, and flush down the drain with lots of water. The methanol from the recrystallization should be placed in the organic solvents container.

THIN LAYER CHROMATOGRAPHY

Run two TLCs—using 2:1 hexane/ether as the eluant. To the first plate, apply two separate spots side-by-side: crude methyl *m*-nitrobenzoate and recrystallized methyl *m*-nitrobenzoate. To the second plate, apply three spots: methyl benzoate on the left, recrystallized methyl *m*-nitrobenzoate on the right, and a mixture of the two (prepared by spotting one compound over the other) in the center. Use a UV light to visualize the spots on your chromatogram. Circle the spots with a pencil.

> **NOTE:** *Make sure that you use very dilute solutions of methyl benzoate and methyl m-nitrobenzoate for spotting the TLC plate. Too much of these compounds applied to the TLC plate will cause streaking and a poor chromatogram.*

> **NOTE:** *Methyl benzoate does not fluoresce very strongly under UV light. Make sure, therefore, that you have spotted enough of this compound to be visible under the UV light.*

Report your crude and purified yields and melting points. Also, calculate the yields of methyl *m*-nitrobenzoate from benzoic acid (overall yield) and from methyl benzoate (yield for second step only). Sketch the TLC plates into your lab notebook and discuss them. Turn in your purified final product.

Questions

1. Why does methyl benzoate dissolve in concentrated sulfuric acid? Write an equation showing the ions that are produced.

2. Why is it important to keep the temperature low during this reaction?

3. If methyl *m*-nitrobenzoate were nitrated a second time, what would the product be and why?

   > **HINT:** *Consider the directing effects of the ester and of the first nitro group on the addition of a second nitro group.*

4. Why is the reaction mixture poured over ice rather than cold water?

5. What is the limiting reagent in this reaction? Why?

6. From your TLC, which is more polar—methyl benzoate or methyl *m*-nitrobenzoate? Why? How did you arrive at this conclusion from your TLC data?

CHAPTER 17

THE IDENTIFICATION OF AN UNKNOWN ORGANIC COMPOUND

Along with the synthesis of organic compounds and the study of reaction mechanisms, organic chemistry also deals with the characterization and structural identification of organic compounds that may be encountered in sources ranging from the product of a laboratory reaction to the isolation of a new natural product from a tropical plant. Sufficient information must be accumulated to establish the structure of the compound in question. A compound will either be identical to a previously described substance, or else its structure will be shown to be that of an entirely new substance.

Today, most information learned about organic compounds is obtained with instrumental methods using various forms of spectroscopy (infrared, ultraviolet, NMR and mass spectroscopy). However, in this course you will primarily be using classical chemical methods to determine the structure of your unknowns. These methods include measuring physical and solubility properties, doing chemical functional group analysis, and preparing functional group derivatives of the unknown compounds. As part of the identification process, you will also confirm your proposed structures by infrared and NMR spectral analysis. Because the identification process does not follow a fixed pattern and will vary considerably with different unknowns, each student will be working independently to determine the structure of his or her unknowns. You should evaluate the physical properties, solubility properties, and spectral data (when provided), and then seek further information to corroborate your proposed structure.

The procedure for determining the structure of an unknown is straightforward and involves the following steps:

1. Determine the unknown's physical properties such as melting point or boiling point, color, odor, and so on. Also carry out an ignition test and a Beilstein test (for halogen).

2. Classify the unknown by its solubility in various solvents.

3. Perform an elemental analysis.

4. Further classify the unknown using chemical tests that are characteristic of the possible functional groups.

5. Determine and analyze the unknown's infrared and ^{1}H-NMR spectra.

6. Confirm the unknown's identity by taking the melting points of one or more synthesized solid derivatives.

The following is a general outline of the procedure that may be followed in gathering evidence for the identification of an unknown substance. Unknowns will be chosen from among the following commonly encountered functional groups: carboxylic acids, alcohols, aldehydes and ketones, amines, esters, ethers, halides, hydrocarbons (both aliphatic and aromatic), nitro compounds, and phenols.

You will be assigned two unknowns. Your first unknown will be identified purely by chemical means. For your second unknown, you will have the advantage of additional structural information through infrared and NMR spectra. Spectral data will either be provided by your instructor, or you may be required to run your own infrared and/or NMR spectra.

After evaluating physical properties, elemental analysis, solubility data, and any spectral data, you will be asked to submit to your instructor a Preliminary Report which will present all of your findings as well as a list of the possible functional groups present. The nature of the functional group that is present in your unknown should be fairly certain before you proceed with classification tests and the preparation of derivatives. See Section V (Preliminary Report).

I. PHYSICAL PROPERTIES AND PRELIMINARY EXAMINATION

A. Melting Point or Boiling Point

If your unknown is a solid, obtain a melting point. Should the melting point range be larger than 2–3°, it may be necessary to recrystallize the solid from a suitable solvent. When taking a melting point, it should be noted whether decomposition occurs (usually indicated by gas evolution and darkening of the solid), or whether sublimation occurs. Some organic substances (*e.g.*, some substituted carboxylic acids) may lose CO_2 on heating, a process known as decarboxylation. This should be noted if it occurs.

If your unknown is a liquid, a boiling point may be taken on as little as a few drops of liquid by using the microboiling point method that you learned in Organic Chemistry Lab I. Determine the boiling point at least twice. If the two values do not agree by ±5°, repeat the determination. Be sure to write the results of all determinations in your lab notebook.

B. Refractive Index

You may wish to determine the refractive index of your unknown liquid using a refractometer. The index of refraction of a liquid is a physical property, which is also used as a criterion of a liquid's purity. See your instructor if you wish to perform this procedure.

C. Physical Examination, Color, Ignition Test

Most organic compounds are white or colorless. Colors ranging from yellow to brown or red may indicate impurities. True color arises from functional groups (called chromophores) such as several conjugated double bonds, azo groups, nitro groups, quinones, etc. A nitro group on its own produces very little color in a compound, but the presence of an accompanying substituent, such as an amino group or a hydroxyl group, may intensify the pale yellow color.

An **ignition test** may be performed in the hood by placing about 0.1 g of the compound on a spatula or porcelain spoon and heating until ignition occurs. The following should be noted:

1. Flammability and nature of flame (*e.g.*, heavily halogenated alkanes may be non-flammable). Note also the color and sootiness of the flame. Aromatic compounds usually burn with a yellow, sooty flame while aliphatic compounds burn with a more clear flame. Generally, the more oxygen in a compound, the more clear or blue the flame.

2. Manner of melting, such as charring, sublimation, or gas evolution.

3. Odor of any gases evolved, *e.g.*, NH_3.

4. Presence or absence of a residue after ignition. The presence of a residue after ignition may indicate the presence of a metal atom in the original compound.

D. Test for Halogen (Beilstein Test)

The Beilstein test is the easiest, simplest, and fastest method for detecting the presence of halogen. Chlorine-, bromine-, and iodine-containing compounds all give a green flame when burned with a copper wire. Fluorine cannot be determined by this test. Although this test cannot differentiate between the three halogens, many compounds can be eliminated from your list of possibilities just by knowing that one of these elements is present. The Beilstein test is very sensitive and gives a positive test even if trace impurities containing a halogen are present. Therefore, use caution in interpreting the results of this test if only a weak green color is observed.

Procedure

Make a small loop in one end of a sturdy piece of copper wire about four inches long. Embed the other end of the wire in a small cork. Adjust the flame of a Bunsen burner until it is completely blue. Heat the loop in the edge of the blue flame until the flame no longer shows any color. Allow the copper loop to cool partially, and then dip it into a little of the compound to be tested and heat it again in the edge of the blue flame. A brilliant, blue-green flame is a positive test for halogen. Continue to clean the copper wire in the flame until a clean blue flame returns before testing another compound.

II. SOLUBILITY CLASSIFICATION

The solubility of an unknown substance should be examined in the following solvents: water, ether, 5% NaOH, 5% NaHCO$_3$, dilute HCl (5%). Reactivity with cold, concentrated sulfuric acid (H$_2$SO$_4$) should also be determined. The accompanying scheme is to be followed in order to place the compound into its appropriate solubility class.

> **NOTE:** *If the compound is water soluble, there is no point to testing its solubility in dilute acid or base. If the compound is water soluble, the pH of the water solution should be checked with pH paper to detect the presence of acidic or basic groups. Solubility generally means a solution of 0.1 g of a solid or 3–4 drops (0.2 mL) of a liquid occurs in 2 mL of solvent. Quantities of sample should be estimated carefully and shaken with the solvent in small, corked test tubes (don't use a cork with concentrated H$_2$SO$_4$).*

Note that virtually all compounds of moderate molecular size that contain a nitrogen or an oxygen atom or a double or triple bond will be protonated by, and therefore dissolved to some extent, in concentrated H$_2$SO$_4$. One may also observe a color change, evolution of heat or similar phenomena with concentrated sulfuric acid. Any evidence of reaction should be taken as a positive test. The reaction with H$_2$SO$_4$ may be slow; the mixture should be stirred for several minutes before reaching a conclusion.

Solubility Groups

Group S₁: Soluble in Water, Soluble in Ether
Compounds containing up to about five carbon atoms—especially those that contain oxygen, nitrogen, or sulfur—are often soluble in both water and ether. However, increasing the number of carbons to five or six frequently results in insolubility or borderline solubility in water, due to the lower polarity of the molecule.

Check the pH (with pH paper) of an aqueous solution of Group S$_1$ compounds. Alkaline readings suggest the presence of an amine, while acidic readings suggest the presence of a carboxylic acid or a sulfonic acid.

Group S₂: Soluble in Water, Insoluble in Ether
Group S$_2$ compounds include polycarboxylic acids and amine salts, which are too polar to dissolve in ether.

Group S$_2$ compounds also include di- and polyfunctional compounds such as carbohydrates, amino acids, and polyhydric alcohols. All of these compounds are also too polar to be soluble in ether.

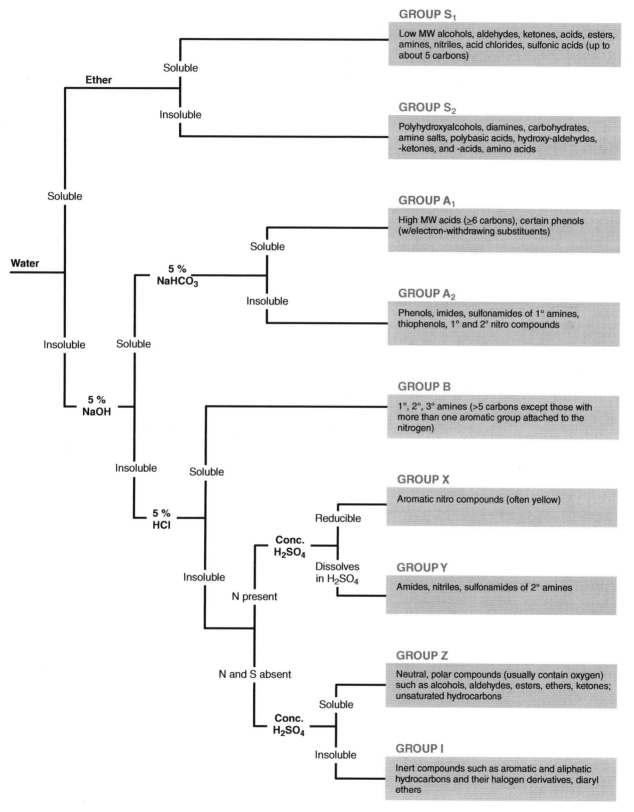

Figure 17-1. *Solubility Flowchart.*

Group A₁: Insoluble in Water, Soluble in 5% NaOH and 5% NaHCO₃

$NaHCO_3$ is a weaker base than NaOH, so compounds that dissolve in 5% $NaHCO_3$ are fairly acidic. This group includes carboxylic acids and sulfonic acids, both of which react with $NaHCO_3$ to form a water-soluble sodium salt. Formation of carbon dioxide results in gas evolution. This serves as evidence that a reaction has occurred.

Most phenols are not acidic enough to react with 5% $NaHCO_3$. If, however, there are one or more strong electron-withdrawing groups on the benzene ring, the phenol will react with $NaHCO_3$ and the phenol will dissolve.

Remember that some phenols—such as phenol itself—are polar enough to dissolve in water and therefore belong in Group S_1.

Group A₂: Insoluble in Water and 5% NaHCO₃, Soluble in 5% NaOH

Some compounds are only weakly acidic and can only be deprotonated by the strongly basic NaOH but not by $NaHCO_3$. These compounds include: phenols, nitroalkanes, sulfonamides of 1° amines, imides, and β-dicarbonyl compounds.

Group B: Insoluble in Water and 5% NaOH, Soluble in 5% HCl

Practically all 1°, 2°, and 3° amines are soluble in 5% HCl. Diaryl and triaryl amines, however, do not dissolve. Although diaryl amines actually do react with 5% HCl, the resulting ammonium salt is not water soluble. Triaryl amines don't react at all with 5% HCl because they are totally nonbasic.

Group X: Insoluble in Water, 5% NaOH, 5% HCl, and Concentrated H₂SO₄, Contain Nitrogen, and Can Be Reduced

Group X includes aromatic nitro compounds, which can be reduced to amines and which are frequently yellow in color.

Group Y: Insoluble in Water, 5% NaOH, and 5% HCl, Soluble in Concentrated H₂SO₄; Contains Nitrogen and Can Be Hydrolyzed

Group Y includes amides, nitriles, and sulfonamides of 2° amines. Even though they are only very weakly basic, they will dissolve in sulfuric acid if it is concentrated. They hydrolyze to form either carboxylic acids or sulfonic acids. For example:

Group Z: Insoluble in Water, 5% NaOH and 5% HCl, but Soluble in Concentrated H₂SO₄

Group Z includes alcohols, aldehydes, ketones, esters, most ethers, alkenes, alkynes, and anhydrides. The reason that they dissolve in concentrated sulfuric acid is that they can be protonated. For example:

Group I: Insoluble in Water, 5% NaOH, 5% HCl and Concentrated H₂SO₄

Group I includes alkyl and aryl halides, many aromatic hydrocarbons, alkanes, and diaryl ethers. Diaryl ethers do not dissolve because the electron pairs on oxygen delocalize into both aromatic rings by resonance and are not available for sharing even with concentrated sulfuric acid. Some aromatic hydrocarbons will dissolve because they are sulfonated by concentrated sulfuric acid.

III. INFRARED AND NMR SPECTRA

For those unknowns where **infrared spectra** are to be used, you will either be given a copy of the IR spectrum of your compound, or your instructor will request that you run your own spectrum according to his/her directions. Not all peaks in the spectrum will be characterized and identified, but the Table on page 140 will be of use in identifying the major peaks and identifying the functional group(s) present in the unknown. Remember, all values for peak positions are approximate. If your background in the theory of infrared spectroscopy is weak, your instructor will amplify it in class. Intelligent use of IR spectra and comparison with literature spectra (such as the "Aldrich Library of Infrared Spectra") can go a long way toward identifying your compound. Do not expect a perfect match, since spectra were recorded on different instruments under differing conditions. Instead, use the spectral comparisons to help distinguish between two or three possibilities.

In the case of ¹H-NMR Spectra, it should be possible to assign all peaks in the spectrum and rationalize how the spectrum is consistent with the structure proposed for your unknown. You should use the principles of NMR spectroscopy that you learned in Organic Chemistry lecture.

IV. ELEMENTAL ANALYSIS (SODIUM FUSION)

Should the results of Parts I, II, and III indicate the strong possibility that heteroatoms are present in your unknown, an elemental analysis may be useful.

The sodium fusion procedure allows for the detection of any nitrogen, sulfur, or halogen that may be present in an organic compound. While this procedure has largely been replaced by the use of mass spectrometry, it is still a useful "wet" laboratory method of determining the presence of heteroatoms.

The sodium fusion process destroys the organic compound and converts any covalently bonded sulfur, nitrogen, or halogen atoms into their ionic form: sulfide (S^{-2}), cyanide ($CN^{\ominus}$), or halide ($X^{\ominus}$) ions respectively. The ions can then be detected by the usual wet tests, which you performed in your inorganic qualitative analysis laboratory.

> **NOTE:** *Do not perform the sodium fusion test without first checking with your instructor.*

The procedure for performing an elemental analysis by sodium fusion is given in the Experimental Procedures section on page 138.

V. PRELIMINARY REPORT

At this point, you should have an idea of the functional group(s) present in your unknown. Your choice of functional groups should be limited to one or two.

So that you will not be working with incorrect assumptions, a preliminary report should be submitted to your instructor at this point. It should contain all findings thus far determined such as physical constants, solubility class, and elemental analysis. The report should indicate which classification tests you intend to perform to confirm the presence of functional groups that were indicated by the data collected so far. This will allow your instructor to inform you of any incorrect or misleading observations that you might have made.

> **NOTE:** *This report will ultimately be part of your final grade for the unknown.*

For your second unknown, you will be given spectral information (NMR and/or IR) after you have submitted your preliminary report.

VI. CLASSIFICATION TESTS

After your graded Preliminary Report has been returned to you and you discuss it with your instructor, you should decide on which classification tests you will run from the following list. At this point, your choice of functional group(s) should be limited to one or two. At *most*, 4–5 such tests should be necessary. Specific instructions for each of the chemical classification tests may be found in the sections beginning on page 154. If you perform any tests that are not outlined in this laboratory manual, they should be appropriately referenced.

Classification Tests

1. *Aldehydes and Ketones*
    a. *2,4-Dinitrophenylhydrazine
    b. Iodoform test
    c. Tollens' reagent
    d. Chromic acid
    e. Schiff's reagent

2. *Alcohols*
    a. Acetyl chloride
    b. Lucas test
    c. Chromic anhydride (Jones oxidation)
    d. Iodoform test
    e. Ceric ammonium nitrate

3. *Amines*
    a. *Hinsberg test
    b. *Acetyl chloride test
    c. Solubility and pH of aqueous solution

4. *Carboxylic Acids*
    a. pH of aqueous solution
    b. Sodium bicarbonate solution
    c. Neutralization equivalent
    d. Silver nitrate (ethanolic)

5. *Esters*
    a. Ferric hydroxamate test

6. *Hydrocarbons*
    a. Bromine in methylene chloride (alkenes)
    b. Baeyer test (potassium permanganate solution)
    c. Anhydrous aluminum chloride in chloroform (aromatic ring)
    d. Sulfuric acid

---

*   Some classification tests produce a solid product which may also be used as a derivative (derivatives are discussed in the next section). The tests which do so are marked with an asterisk (*). In those cases, any solid product obtained should be isolated and saved for possible use as a derivative.

7. *Nitro Compounds*

  a. Zinc and ammonium chloride test

  b. Sodium hydroxide color test

8. *Phenols*

  a. Solubility in sodium hydroxide solution

  b. Ferric chloride test

  c. Ceric nitrate test

  d. *Acetyl chloride

  e. *Bromine water

Before coming to the lab, you should spend some time thinking about which tests would be advantageous to perform. Then write in your laboratory notebook: the procedure to be used, what a positive or negative test looks like, and what the limitations of the test are. Reviewing the previous several experiments where you performed the classification tests on compounds of known structure will help prepare you for testing your unknown. If you are thus prepared, you can come to the lab and do the tests while making the most effective use of your time.

VII. DERIVATIVES

Derivatives are solid crystalline substances which are prepared to confirm the identity of an unknown compound.

You are to prepare one or two derivatives of your unknown to confirm its structure. A sample of each derivative is to be handed in with your final report. How does one pick a derivative? What are the criteria for a good derivative? An example will illustrate this:

Your unknown had a boiling point of 235° ±5° and appeared to be a ketone. The following list of ketones which boil from 230°–240° are possibilities:

	b.p.	m.p. Oxime	m.p. Semicarbazone
Phenyl-*n*-propyl ketone	230°	50°(*)	284°
p-Chloroacetophenone	232°	95°	201°(*)
Methyl β-phenylethyl ketone	235°	85°	142°
m-Methoxyacetophenone	240°	— (*)	196°(*)

The melting points (°C) of the possible derivatives are given. The *poor* choices are starred (*).

To choose the proper derivative, read vertically to see the melting points of the same derivative of different compounds. To be certain of the identification of a compound, the melting points of the derivatives should be different by at least ten degrees because you assume a melting point accuracy of ±5°. To clearly identify your unknown as either *p*-chloroacetophenone or *m*-methoxyacetophenone, a semicarbazone derivative would be of no value *unless* you know a halogen is present. If halogen *is* present, either the semicarbazone or oxime derivative may be chosen for confirmation of the unknown. If halogen is absent, then the semicarbazone would be the best derivative to distinguish among the remaining possibilities.

The oxime would be a poor derivative to distinguish among the four compounds for the following reasons: (1) There is no oxime listed for *m*-methoxyacetophenone. This does not mean that it cannot be made, just that it has not been reported and cannot be used for identification. (2) The oxime of phenyl *n*-propyl ketone melts at 50°. If possible, try to avoid choosing derivatives melting below 80° as these tend to form oils and may be hard to crystallize when you prepare them.

In some instances, choices may not work out so neatly as in this case. However, you are expected to use your best judgment in choosing a derivative to prepare. In the preparation of the derivative, save a small amount of the initial crystals to use as seed crystals, just in case your derivative does not crystallize easily. If a broad melting range is obtained, the derivative should be recrystallized from an appropriate solvent. Derivatives prepared or crystallized from water solutions should be dried thoroughly (for a few days) before a melting point is determined. However, to save time, small amounts may be dried by pressing them between filter papers and spreading them out in the air.

The following is a summary of the common derivatives of each functional group. Preparative procedures for these derivatives can be found in this laboratory manual. Tables of compounds and some of their known derivatives can be found at the end of this lab manual.

Aldehydes and Ketones	phenyl-, *p*-nitrophenyl-, or 2,4-dinitrophenylhydrazones; oximes or semicarbazones
Alcohols	3,5-dinitrobenzoates, phenyl- or 1-naphthylurethanes
Amines	
Primary and Secondary	benzene- or *p*-toluenesulfonamides; acetamides, benzamides, or phenylthioureas
Tertiary	addition compounds with methyl tosylate, methyl iodide, or picric acid
Carboxylic Acids	amides or anilides; *p*-nitrobenzyl or *p*-bromophenacyl esters
Esters	hydrolysis products
Ethers (Aromatic)	nitro or bromo substitution products
Halides	anilides
Hydrocarbons (Aromatic)	picrates, nitro derivatives or aroylbenzoic acids
Nitro Compounds	reduce to corresponding amine (see Amines) and prepare *p*-toluenesulfonamides, benzamides, or acetamides
Phenols	acetates, benzoates, 1-naphthylurethanes, or bromo-derivatives

In addition, amides, nitriles, acetals, acid chlorides, and acid anhydrides can all be hydrolyzed to carboxylic acids, amines, and alcohols and identified using derivatives of the hydrolysis products.

VIII. GRADING

Your instructor will discuss grading in detail, but in general, you will receive two grades for each unknown.

The first grade will be for the preliminary report, which discusses the nature of the possible functional group(s) present in your unknown and outlines your next course of action. This grade will encompass the proper evaluation of solubility results, proper determination of physical constants, elemental analysis, and any other information gathered.

The second grade will result from the proper logic used in deciding the structure of your unknown, the use and interpretation of classification tests, and the proper preparation and purification of a derivative. The notebook write-up should also include the spectra utilized and their detailed interpretation, chemical equations for the reactions that were employed in your work, comments and observations on the results of the various tests, and a discussion of how the final structure was determined. Please note carefully the title and page number of any references used in your experimentation. More consideration will be given to whether the reported structure was derived logically from all of the experimental data than to whether the reported structure is actually the correct one.

Experimental Procedures

Solubility Classification

The solubility of the unknown substance is to be examined in the following solvents: **water, ether, 5% NaOH, 5% NaHCO$_3$, 5% HCl, and cold concentrated sulfuric acid (H$_2$SO$_4$)** as follows:

a. *Solubility in Water*

Determine if the unknown substance is soluble in water. *If soluble in water*, determine the approximate pH of the water solution using pH paper. Speculate as to the **polarity** of your unknown substance based on its water solubility.

b. *Solubility in Ether*

   If the unknown substance is soluble in water, determine its solubility in ether. (Is ether more or less polar than water?)

   NOTE: *Organic acids and bases can be distinguished from other functional groups by their ability to be converted to water soluble salts. Solubility in 5% NaHCO$_3$ solution with evolution of CO$_2$ gas generally indicates strong organic acids; solubility in 5% NaOH but not 5% NaHCO$_3$ indicates a weak acid such as a phenol or an enol. Organic bases such as amines are generally soluble in dilute HCl, forming ammonium salts.*

c. *Solubility in 5% NaOH*

   If the unknown substance is insoluble in water, determine its solubility in 5% NaOH.

d. *Solubility in 5% NaHCO$_3$*

   If the unknown is soluble in 5% NaOH, determine its solubility in 5% NaHCO$_3$. (Remember that NaHCO$_3$ is less basic than NaOH. Would your unknown therefore be more acidic or less acidic?)

e. *Solubility in 5% HCl*

   If the unknown is insoluble in 5% NaOH, determine its solubility in 5% HCl.

f. *Solubility in Cold, Concentrated H$_2$SO$_4$*

   If the unknown is insoluble in 5% HCl, determine its solubility in cold, concentrated H$_2$SO$_4$.

   NOTE: *Virtually all compounds of moderate molecular size that contain a nitrogen or an oxygen atom or a double or triple bond are protonated by, and therefore dissolve to some extent, in concentrated H$_2$SO$_4$. One may observe a color change, evolution of heat, or similar phenomenon with concentrated sulfuric acid. Any evidence of reaction should be taken as a positive test. The reaction with H$_2$SO$_4$ may be slow; the mixture should be stirred for several minutes before reaching a conclusion.*

Refer to the Solubility Flowchart on page 129 to help you decide what the functional group might be in your unknown.

Sodium Fusion Procedure

> *CAUTION: Sodium metal reacts violently with water to produce hydrogen gas. Handle sodium only with clean, **dry** utensils, forceps, knife or spatula. Keep sodium metal away from water and destroy any waste with anhydrous ethanol or with 1-butanol.*

> *Work in the fume hood.*

> ***Wear safety glasses!** Molten sodium in the eyes can cause blindness.*

1. Remove one sodium "sphere" from the storage bottle and place it on a piece of paper towel. Cut it in half and return the unused portion to the storage bottle at once. Place the freshly cut piece of sodium into a clean, dry, 3-inch test tube.

2. Your instructor will show you how to clamp or otherwise support the test tube. A clamp with no rubber coating will do.

3. Using a Bunsen burner, heat the lower part of the test tube until the sodium melts and sodium vapors rise about 1/3 of the way up the test tube. Be sure that the bottom of the test tube is in the hottest part of the flame. The bottom of the tube will likely have a red glow.

4. Remove the tube from the flame and *immediately* add about 10 mg of your solid unknown (a pinch from the spatula, or 2 small drops if the unknown is a liquid) *directly onto the molten sodium.* The sample must hit the sodium directly and not adhere to the side of the tube. A flash or small explosion will likely occur.

   > *CAUTION: Safety glasses must be worn, and the face should be kept away from the mouth of the tube, as some compounds react violently with the molten sodium.*

5. Heat the tube again until the sodium vapors rise, and add a second 10 mg portion of your unknown as before. Heat slowly until the sodium vapors rise again, then heat the test tube to a red heat for at least three minutes.

6. *While it is still hot*, plunge the tube into a 50 mL beaker containing 15 mL of **distilled** water.

   > *CAUTION: The test tube should break by the thermal shock. Break up the pieces using a glass stirring rod.*

7. Heat the contents of the beaker to boiling, and gravity filter. Wash the residue with 4 mL of hot **distilled** water, filter, and add the washings to the filtrate. *The filtrate should be colorless and clear.* A slight yellow color is acceptable. If the filtrate is very dark, the sodium fusion should be repeated as this dark color will mask the tests. The clear filtrate is used for the specific tests which follow.

    NOTE: *To verify that acceptable conversion to inorganic ions has taken place, a small sample (3–4 drops) of the filtrate can be acidified with dilute HNO_3 and reacted with a few drops of $AgNO_3$ solution. Examine the precipitate. AgCl and AgCN are white, AgBr is cream, AgI is yellow and Ag_2S is black.*

    NOTE ALSO: *What can you infer if no precipitate forms?*

Test for Sulfur

a. Acidify 1 mL of the stock solution with glacial acetic acid in a small test tube, and add 2 drops of a 1% solution of lead(II) acetate. Formation of a brown-black precipitate of lead sulfide (PbS) indicates the presence of sulfur.

b. *Sodium nitroprusside test*: Make a fresh solution by dissolving one crystal of sodium nitroprusside in 2–3 mL of **distilled** water. Add 2 drops of this solution to 1 mL of the stock solution. A reddish-violet coloration (which fades on standing) indicates the presence of sulfur.

Test for Nitrogen

The sodium fusion procedure has converted organic nitrogen into cyanide ion, $CN^\ominus$, which is detected by conversion into the dark blue, insoluble ferri/ferrocyanide ion (Prussian Blue).

Using pH paper and a 10% sodium hydroxide solution, adjust the pH of about 1 mL of the stock solution to pH 13. Add 2 drops of saturated ferrous ammonium sulfate solution and 2 drops of 30% potassium fluoride solution. Boil the solution for about 30 seconds. Then acidify the hot solution by adding 30% sulfuric acid dropwise until the iron hydroxide dissolves. Avoid using excess acid. If nitrogen is present, a dark blue (not green) precipitate of Prussian blue, $NaFe_2(CN)_6$, will form, or the solution will assume a dark blue color.

> **NOTE:** *Nitro groups frequently give poor results with this test. Therefore, if you suspect the presence of a nitro group in your unknown but get a negative result from the sodium fusion test for nitrogen, you should carry out the **Ferrous Hydroxide Test** (see page 181).*

Tests for Halogens

Use half of your remaining stock solution for the halide tests and proceed as follows:

To Determine If Halide is Present: Acidify the solution with dilute nitric acid, and boil it *in the hood* for about 2 minutes. This will drive off any HCN or H_2S that is formed.

> **NOTE:** *This step is necessary because cyanide and sulfide ions interfere with the tests for halide and must therefore be removed in this way if nitrogen and/or sulfur are present in your unknown.*

When the solution cools, add three drops of a 5% $AgNO_3$ solution. A **voluminous** white or yellow precipitate indicates halide ion since AgCl is white, AgBr is cream colored, and AgI is yellow. A dark precipitate means sulfur is present, or the solution has not been properly acidified. If you receive a voluminous white or cream precipitate, move on to the next procedure to determine which halide is present.

To Determine Which Halide is Present: Acidify 2 mL of the test solution with 10% sulfuric acid, and boil it *in the hood* for about two minutes. Cool the solution and add about 0.5 mL of methylene chloride (dichloromethane). Add a few drops of chlorine water* or 2–4 mg of calcium hypochlorite. Check to be sure that the solution is still acidic. Then stopper the tube, shake it vigorously, and set it aside to allow the layers to separate. A yellow, orange or red-brown color in the methylene chloride (lower) layer indicates bromine. Violet or pink indicates iodine. No color or a very pale yellow-green color indicates the absence of bromine or iodine. Hence, the halogen is chlorine.

---

* To prepare a fresh solution of chlorine-water, place a single crystal of potassium chlorate ($KClO_3$) in a clean 6" test tube. Discard any unused $KClO_3$ down the drain with plenty of water. Add 6 mL of concentrated HCl to the test tube, and fill with water. Store in or under the hood.

CHAPTER 18

Spectroscopy in Structure Identification—Infrared and Proton NMR Spectroscopy

INFRARED SPECTROSCOPY

Atoms in a molecule do not maintain fixed positions with respect to each other, but constantly vibrate back and forth. The two basic types of bond vibration are bending and stretching. Absorption of infrared light of the appropriate energy "excites" a molecule from its ground state to a second vibrational level, which is higher in energy than the first. The frequency or wavelength of light that is absorbed depends on the relative masses of the atoms, the force constants of the bonds, and the geometry of the vibrations between the atoms. Not all vibrational frequencies result in an observable peak in the infrared spectrum; only those in which a change in dipole moment accompanies the stretching or bending motion can be observed. As a result, the more polar or unsymmetrical a bond, the more intense will be the peak that appears in the infrared spectrum.

By recording and observing the various frequencies that are absorbed by a molecule when subjected to infrared radiation, it is possible to determine the presence of specific functional groups in that molecule.

For many years infrared spectroscopy was the primary spectroscopic tool in qualitative organic structural analysis. It has been supplanted for this purpose in large measure by NMR spectroscopy—especially in the analysis of alkane, alkene, and alkyne C–H functionality. Infrared spectroscopy, however, is still the only rapid and effective method for looking at functional groups such as carbonyls, nitriles, nitro groups, azides, and other multiply bonded heteroatoms that cannot be detected very easily in other ways. The structural features of ethers can be identified by the presence of a characteristic C–O–C absorption. The shift of the position in a carbonyl group absorption can be used to indicate changes in the size of the ring of cyclic ketones, cyclic esters (lactones) and cyclic amides (lactams). Conjugation between C=O and unsaturated groups such as C=C and Ar are also detected by infrared spectroscopy.

An abbreviated list of commonly encountered infrared absorptions is given in the table below. Carbonyl stretching frequencies may deviate by ±10 cm^{-1} due to variations in molecular structure; H-bonding to oxygen can cause shifts as great as 50 cm^{-1}. Conjugation with a carbonyl group causes shifts from 20 to 40 cm^{-1}. Ring strain can also cause shifts from 10 to 40 cm^{-1} depending upon the size of the ring.

Infrared Table of Functional Groups or Types of Bonds	
	Wavenumber (cm^{-1})
Alkane –C–H stretch	2,850–2,960 (s)
Methyl –C–H bend (a double peak when dimethyl)	1,380 (s)
–C=C stretch	1,620–1,680 (v)
Alkene and aromatic –C–H stretch	3,000–3,100 (m)
Alkyne –C≡C–stretch	2,100–2,260 (v)
Alkyne –C–H stretch	3,200–3,300 (s)
–C≡N, N=C=O C=C=O and similar groups	2,000–2,300 (v)
Aldehyde –C=O	1,720–1,740 (s)
Aldehyde –C–H	2,695–2,830 (two moderate bands)
Nitriles –C≡N	2,240–2,260 (m)
Ester –C=O	1,735–1,750 (s)
Acid chloride –C=O	1,800 (s)
Ketone –C=O	1,705–1,725 (s)
Acid anhydride –C=O	1,760 and 1,800–1,850 (v)
Carboxylic acid –COOH	1,700–1,725 and 2,500–3,000 (b)
OH stretch, H-bonded (intermolecular)	3,200–3,400 (s,b)
NH stretch (a doublet when –NH$_2$)	3,300–3,500 (m)
Characteristic C=C multiple bond stretches	690–880 (m) and 1,450, 1,500, 1,580, 1,600, and 1,660–2,000 (w)
Nitro group C–NO$_2$	1,300–1,380 (s) and 1,500–1,570 (s)
Aliphatic ether C–O–C	1,085–1,150 (s)
Aromatic ether Ar–O–C	1,200–1,275 (s)
s = strong m = medium w = weak v = variable b = broad	

The following vinylic C–H out-of-plane bending vibrations are all strong and can be useful:

a. RCH=CH   995–985 and 915–905 cm^{-1}

b. RCH=CHR' (*cis*)   730–665 cm^{-1}

c. RCH=CHR' (*trans*)   980–960 cm^{-1}

d. R(R')C=CH$_2$ 895–885 cm^{-1}

Aromatic C–H bending substitution patterns range from strong to weak, and all can vary within the ranges given below.

a. Monosubstituted rings   750 and 700 cm^{-1}

b. *ortho*-Disubstitution   770–735 cm^{-1}

c. *meta*-Disubstitution   810–750 and 710–690 cm^{-1}

d. *para*-Disubstitution   840–810 cm^{-1}

In addition to the primary aromatic C–H bending vibrations given above, very weak combination and overtone bands may also be observed in the 2000–1667 cm^{-1} region.

METHODS OF SAMPLE PREPARATION

Qualitative analysis by infrared spectroscopy can be performed as:

1. thin liquid film between salt plates (neat),

2. solutions in inert solvents,

3. dispersions of the sample in Nujol or $CHBr_3$ (a mull), and

4. as a solid dispersion in KBr powder produced under pressure (pellet).

Sample Cells

Since glass strongly absorbs infrared radiation, the cells or windows that are used to hold a chemical sample for IR analysis are fabricated from inorganic salts such as NaCl, KBr, and AgCl. The first two are easily damaged by even small amounts of moisture and can be completely destroyed by water in larger amounts. The AgCl cells are light sensitive. For this reason caution must always be exercised when using this equipment.

Sample Preparation

Spectra of pure liquids are obtained from **neat** or undiluted samples. One simply places a drop of the pure liquid between two salt plates and mounts them in an appropriate sample holder. In the case of solids, two options are commonly used. A **mull** may be prepared by grinding the sample in an agate mortar with a drop or two of Nujol (a type of purified mineral oil) or $CHBr_3$. This suspension is then placed between the salt plates and mounted in an appropriate sample holder (see Figure 18-1). Since it is a hydrocarbon, Nujol contains several strong absorptions which can obscure parts of the spectrum. To circumvent this problem, one usually prepares a second mull in $CHBr_3$. Another option for preparing a solid sample is to dissolve the solid in a few drops of CCl_4 or CS_2, place a drop of the resulting solution between two salt plates, and mount the plates in an appropriate sample holder (see below). Carbon tetrachloride has absorption bands that obscure the region below 900 cm^{-1}. If it is necessary to see this region of the spectrum, a second spectrum using CS_2 as the solvent is also taken.

> **NOTE:** Caution should be exercised when using CCl_4; it is toxic. Such samples should be prepared in a hood.

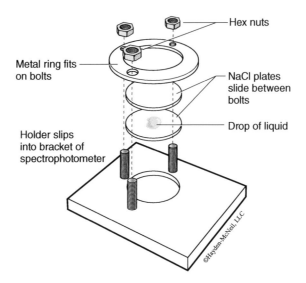

Figure 18-1. *Assembly of Liquid Sample between NaCl Plates.*

Another method is to prepare a solution of the material in CCl_4 or CS_2 and place it into a so-called solution cell (see Figure 18-2). This cell consists of a pair of salt plates that are held apart by a spacer made of an inert material such as Teflon. The size of the spacer can be changed to regulate the thickness of the sample. The sample is introduced with a dropper or syringe, and the openings to the cell are then tightly sealed in order to prevent the sample from leaking out or evaporating. The solution cell technique has another advantage. A duplicate cell can be filled with the pure solvent and placed in the reference beam of the spectrometer in order to cancel out the solvent absorptions. Only the spectrum of the solute, therefore, is observed.

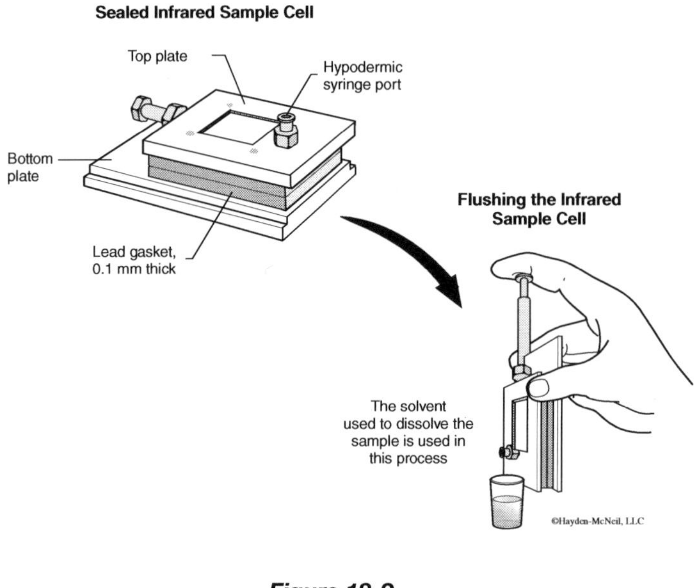

Sealed Infrared Sample Cell

Top plate

Hypodermic
syringe port

Bottom
plate

**Flushing the Infrared
Sample Cell**

Lead gasket,
0.1 mm thick

The solvent
used to dissolve the
sample is used in
this process

©Hayden-McNeil, LLC

Figure 18-2.

A sometimes serious problem with taking a spectrum as a Nujol mull is that some solids can produce films that are quite opaque, thus producing a poor spectrum. The most frequently employed alternative is the KBr pellet. One to two milligrams of a solid sample are ground in an agate mortar with 50 to 100 milligrams of very dry spectral grade KBr. There are several types of presses available which will compress the mixture into a translucent pellet. The most common press available for student use is the KBr Mini-press, shown in Figure 18-3. Your instructor will demonstrate the use of the press as well as the care required in handling it.

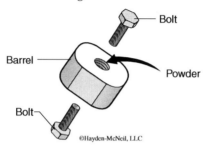

Figure 18-3. *KBr Mini-press.*

NOTE: *When not in use, all cells should be stored in a desiccator. KBr for pellets should be stored in an oven so that it will always be dry.*

ANALYZING AN INFRARED SPECTRUM

Most infrared spectra consist of a complex array of peaks. This situation can be very frustrating to the novice in infrared interpretation. However, with a bit of practice, one learns to identify several of the peaks in a spectrum as being characteristic of the presence of particular structural features (*i.e.*, the functional groups) in the molecule. Do not hesitate to refer to books and tables as much as needed in your early attempts at spectral interpretation. You will find your skills improve rapidly with practice.

In trying to analyze the spectrum of an unknown, you should concentrate first on trying to establish the presence (or absence) of a few major functional groups. The most conspicuous peaks are C=O, O–H, N–H, C–O, C=C, C≡C, C≡N, and NO_2. If they are present, they give immediate structural information. Do not try to analyze in detail the CH absorptions near 3000 cm^{-1}; almost all organic compounds produce these absorptions. Do not worry about subtleties of the exact environment in which the functional group is found. A checklist of the important gross features follows.

1. *Check for a carbonyl group.* The C=O group gives a strong absorption in the region of 1820–1660 cm^{-1}. The peak is often the strongest one in the spectrum.

2. *If a carbonyl group is present,* check for the following peaks:

    a. *Carboxylic Acid:* Look for an O–H absorption. Check for a very broad, usually strong peak in the range of 3300–2500 cm^{-1}. This peak usually overlaps with any C–H absorption peaks.

b. *Aldehyde:* Look for the C–H absorption of the –CHO group. Check for two medium to weak peaks at 2850 and 2750 cm⁻¹. The peak at 2850 cm⁻¹ is often obscured.

c. *Amide:* Look for an N–H absorption. Check for a narrow or broad, medium peak at 3500 cm⁻¹. The absorption will sometimes appear as two peaks, depending on whether the amide is 1° (2 peaks) or 2° (one peak). Tertiary (3°) amides, of course, show no N–H absorption.

d. *Anhydride:* Look for a double C=O absorption. Check for two peaks near 1810 and 1760 cm⁻¹.

e. *Ester:* In addition to the strong C=O peak, look for a C–O absorption. Check for one or two medium intensity peaks in the region of 1300–1000 cm⁻¹.

f. *Ketone:* This functional group is assigned by eliminating possibilities a–e.

3. a. *Alcohols and Phenols:* Look for an O–H absorption. Check for a strong, broad peak in the region 3600–3200 cm⁻¹. Confirm by finding a C–O peak near 1300–1000 cm⁻¹.

   b. *Amine:* Look for N-H absorptions. Check for one (for a 2° amine) or two (for a 1° amine) medium (sometimes broad) peaks at 3550–3060 cm⁻¹.

   c. *Alkyl Ether:* Look for a C–O absorption. One peak in the region of 1150–1085 cm⁻¹. Be sure there is no O–H peak.

   d. *Alkyl/Aryl Ether:* Look for C–O absorptions. Check for one peak at 1275–1200 cm⁻¹ and one peak at 1075–1020 cm⁻¹. Be sure there is no O–H peak.

4. *Alkene:* Look for a C=C absorption. Check for a weak to medium peak near 1650 cm⁻¹ (not always visible). Also, look for a weak vinyl C–H peak just to the left of 3000 cm⁻¹.

5. *Aromatic Ring:* Look for an aromatic ring C=C bond absorption. There should be a medium to strong peak near 1600 cm⁻¹ and one peak at 1450 cm⁻¹ or for two peaks at 1500 and 1450 cm⁻¹. Also check for weak to medium aromatic C–H peaks just the to left of 3000 cm⁻¹.

6. *Alkyne:* Look for a C≡C absorption. Check for a sharp, weak peak near 2150 cm⁻¹. Also, for a terminal alkyne, check for a medium to strong acetylenic C–H peak near 3300 cm⁻¹.

7. *Nitro Group:* Look for an N=O absorption. Check for two strong peaks at 1600–1500 cm⁻¹ and 1390–1300 cm⁻¹.

8. *Nitrile:* Look for a C≡N triple bond. Check for a weak, sharp peak at 2260–2150 cm⁻¹.

9. *Alkane:* Look for sp³ C–H absorptions. Check for several strong peaks just to the right of 3000 cm⁻¹ and medium peaks near 1450 cm⁻¹ and 1375 cm⁻¹. An alkane with no functional groups will have a very simple spectrum with few if any other peaks.

¹H-NMR SPECTROSCOPY

In trying to analyze a proton NMR spectrum, you should focus on three features: chemical shift, integration, and peak splitting—in that order.

Chemical Shift

In most cases, you will see a specific absorption at a different position on the spectrum for each different (magnetically nonequivalent) type of proton in the molecule. Remember that chemical shift depends on the degree of shielding or deshielding felt by a given proton. The two major factors that affect shielding are (1) the proximity of a proton to electronegative atoms, and (2) the anisotropic effect of π-bonds, aromatic ring currents, etc. which creates regions of shielding and deshielding in the vicinity of a given proton. A table of common chemical shifts is given on page 149.

Integration

The **size** of a peak in a proton NMR spectrum is proportional to the number of protons causing that absorption. Specifically, "size" refers to the area under a peak (or the total area under a group of peaks) and is referred to as the "integral" of the peak or, simply, "the integration."

Peak Splitting

A given absorption in a proton NMR spectrum may be **split** into a number of peaks via interaction of a given proton with neighboring, nonequivalent protons. The magnitude of the splitting is referred to as the coupling constant, "J," and is given in units of Hertz (Hz). Splitting is usually classified by the number of sigma bonds between the protons that are coupled to one another. For example, splitting between protons that are two sigma bonds apart is designated as ²J-coupling and is called **geminal coupling**; splitting between protons that are three sigma bonds apart is designated as ³J-coupling and is called vicinal coupling. ⁴J-Coupling (between protons with four intervening bonds) is usually very small (or zero) except where there are intervening π-bonds. In those instances, ⁴J-(and in some instances even ⁵J) coupling constants may be visible. Such coupling is referred to as **long-range coupling**. The table on page 152 lists common ²J-, ³J, and ⁴J-coupling constants.

Another factor affecting the magnitude of the coupling constant between two different protons is the angle between them. These angular relationships are shown in the graphs below. The first graph shows the relationship between the coupling constant and the dihedral angle between two protons with a vicinal relationship. The second graph shows the relationship between the coupling constant and the H–C–H bond angle between two protons with a geminal relationship.

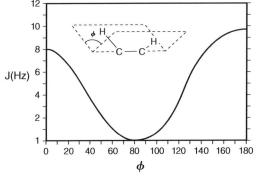

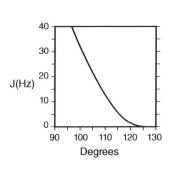

Vicinal Karplus Correlation
Relationship between dihedral angle (ϕ)
and coupling constant for vicinal protons

Geminal Karplus Correlation
J_{HH} for CH_2 groups as a
function of HCH bond angle

Splitting is caused by the fact that each proton can sense the spin state of neighboring protons. In general, the signal for protons coupled equally to n equivalent neighboring protons will be split into **multiplets** having (n+1) lines. This is referred to as **first order splitting**. The intensities of the individual lines in the multiplets follow Pascal's Triangle (shown below).

Singlet						1						
Triplet					1	2	1					
Quartet				1	3		3	1				
Quintet			1	4		6		4	1			
Sextet		1	5		10		10		5	1		
Septet	1	6		15		20		15		6	1	

First order splitting will be observed if $\Delta\nu/J>10$; that is, if the difference in the chemical shift ($\Delta\nu$ in Hz) divided by the coupling constant (J in Hz) is ten or greater. As $\Delta\nu/J$ decreases from ten, multiplets become increasingly distorted, new lines may appear, and lines can merge or disappear. Such undecipherable patterns are referred to as **second order splitting**. This phenomenon is shown in Diagram A which depicts a so-called A_2B_2 system of protons (2 equivalent protons vicinal to 2 other equivalent protons). The diagram shows a series of spectra in which $\Delta\nu/J$ decreases when going from the bottom spectrum to the top spectrum. Notice how first order splitting (in the bottom spectrum) gradually deteriorates into unpredictable splitting patterns.

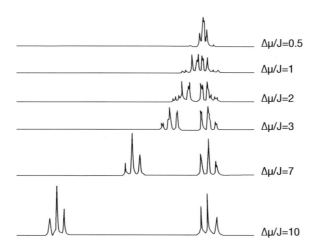

Diagram A: an A$_2$B$_2$ system of protons. Systems of protons with varying Δμ/J.

Representative Proton Chemical Shift Values

Name	Type of Proton	Chemical Shift (δ)
1° Alkyl	R — CH$_3$	0.8 – 1.0
2° Alkyl	R — CH$_2$ — R	1.2 – 1.5
3° Alkyl	R$_3$C — H	1.4 – 1.7
Vinyl	C=C — H	4.6 – 5.9
Allyl	C=C – CH$_2$ — H	1.6 – 1.9
Acetylenic	C≡C — H	2.3 – 2.5
Aromatic	Ar — H	6.0 – 8.5
Benzylic	Ar — CH$_3$	2.2 – 2.5
Alcohol (OH)	R — OH	1.0 – 5.5
Alcohol (α-CH)	HO — CH	3.4 – 4.0
Alcohol (β-CH)	HO — CH$_2$CH	1.2 – 1.6

Phenol (OH)	Ar — **OH**	4.0 – 12
Amino (NH)	R — **NH₂**	0.6 – 2.5
Alkylamino (α-CH)	R₂N — **CH**CH₃	2.5 – 2.8
Alkylamino (β-CH)	R₂N — CH₂**CH₃**	1.0 – 1.3
Arylamino (NH)	Ar — **NH₂**	3.0 – 4.5
Arylamino (α-CH)	ArNH — **CH₃**	3.0 – 3.3
Alkyl ether (α-CH)	R — O**CH₃**	3.2 – 3.5
Alkyl ether (β-CH)	ROCH₂**CH₃**	1.2 – 1.4
Alkyl ether (γ-CH)	RO — CH₂**CH₂**CH₃	0.9 – 1.1
Aryl ether (α-CH)	Ar — O**CH₃**	3.7 – 4.0
Alkyl ketone (α-CH)	R — C(=O) — **CH₃**	2.1 – 2.4
Alkyl ketone (β-CH)	R — C(=O) — CH₂**CH₃**	1.1 – 1.4
Aryl ketone (α-CH)	Ar — C(=O) — **CH₃**	2.4 – 2.6
Aldehyde (-CHO)	R — C(=O) — **H**	9.4 – 9.9
Alkyl aldehyde (α-CH)	H — C(=O) — **CH₃**	2.1 – 2.4
Alkyl aldehyde (β-CH)	H — C(=O) — CH₂**CH₃**	1.1 – 1.4
Alkyl ester (α-CH)	RO — C(=O) — **CH₃**	9.7 – 10.3
Alkyl ester (β-CH)	RO — C(=O) — CH₂**CH₃**	1.2 – 1.4
Alkyl ester (O-CH)	RO — C(=O) — O**CH₂CH₃**	3.7 – 4.1

Carboxylic acid (OH)	$R - \overset{\overset{\displaystyle O}{\|\|}}{C} - OH$	10.4 – 12.0
Carboxylic acid (α-CH)	$HO - \overset{\overset{\displaystyle O}{\|\|}}{C} - CH_2R$	2.2 – 4.4
Carboxylic acid (β-CH)	$HO - \overset{\overset{\displaystyle O}{\|\|}}{C} - CH_2CH_3$	1.0 – 1.4
Aryl carboxylic acid (OH)	$Ar - \overset{\overset{\displaystyle O}{\|\|}}{C} - OH$	10.4 – 12.0
Amide (NH)	$R - \overset{\overset{\displaystyle O}{\|\|}}{C} - NH_2$	5.5 – 7.5
Amide (α-CH)	$NH_2 - \overset{\overset{\displaystyle O}{\|\|}}{C} - CH_2R$	1.8 – 2.2
Amide (N-CH)	$R - \overset{\overset{\displaystyle O}{\|\|}}{C} - NH - CH_3$	2.8 – 3.0
Alkyl chloride (α-CH)	$R - CH_2 - Cl$	0.8 – 1.0
Alkyl chloride (β-CH)	$Cl - CH_2C\underline{H}_3$	1.6 – 1.8
Dichloromethane (CH_2Cl_2)	Cl_2CH_2	5.30
Chloroform ($CHCl_3$)	Cl_3CH	7.27
Alkyl bromide (α-CH)	$R - CH_2 - Br$	3.2 – 3.4
Alkyl bromide (β-CH)	$Br - CH_2C\underline{H}_3$	1.6 – 1.8
Alkyl iodide (α-CH)	$R - CH_2 - I$	3.0 – 3.3
Alkyl iodide (β-CH)	$I - CH_2C\underline{H}_3$	1.7 – 1.9
Alkyl fluoride (α-CH)	$R - CH_2 - F$	4.2 – 4.5
Alkyl fluoride (β-CH)	$F - CH_2 CH_3$	1.4 – 1.6
Enol	$C = C - OH$	1.5 – 1.7
Alkyl thiol (SH)	$R - SH$	1.0 – 2.0
Nitrile (α-CH)	$N \equiv C - CH_2 - R$	2.0 – 2.3
Alkylnitro (α-CH)	$O_2N - CH_2 - R$	4.2 – 4.6

COMMON ^{1}H – ^{1}H COUPLING CONSTANTS

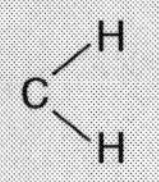

^{2}J = 12 - 15

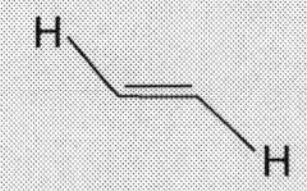

^{3}J = 6 - 8

^{3}J = 8 - 14 (a,a)
^{3}J = 0 - 7 (a,e)
^{3}J = 0 - 5 (e,e)

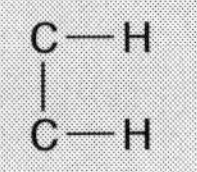

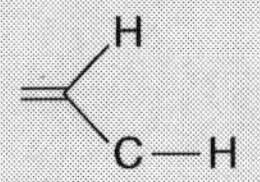

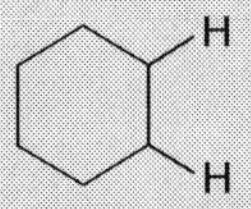

^{3}J = 6 - 10 (ortho)

^{4}J = 1 - 4 (meta)

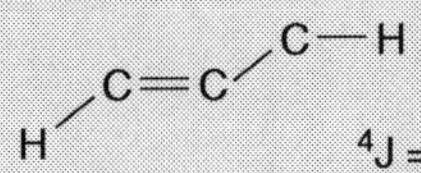

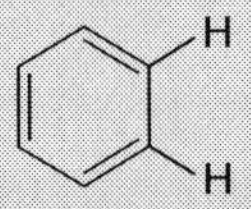

^{5}J = 0 - 2 (para)

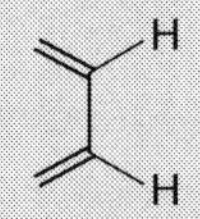

^{2}J = 0 - 5

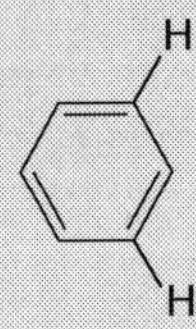

^{3}J = 6 - 15

^{3}J = 11 - 18

^{3}J = 4 - 10

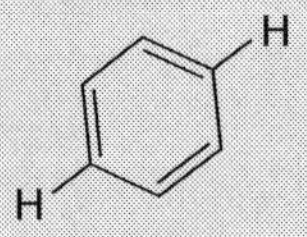

^{4}J = 0 - 3

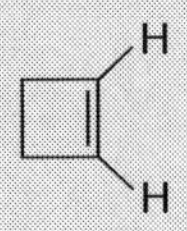

^{3}J = 9 - 13

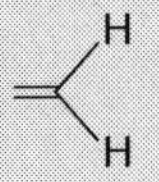

^{3}J = 0 - 2

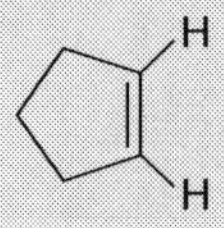

^{3}J = 2.4

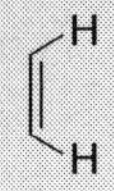

^{3}J = 5 - 7

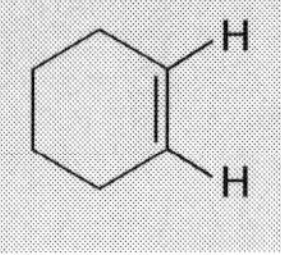

^{3}J = 8 - 11

CHAPTER 19

The Chemistry of the Functional Groups— Classification Tests

The following experiments highlight some important reactions of the most common functional groups. The purpose of these experiments is to provide you with an introduction to wet chemical analysis and to give you a better understanding of functional group chemistry.

Pay close attention to each test and each reaction, because they will form the basis of the **classification tests** that you will be performing when you are given unknown compounds to identify. Be aware of negative results as well as positive ones. Obtaining a negative result from a classification test can often be just as informative as a positive one. On the other hand, some tests will give a positive result with more than one type of functional group. Therefore, when dealing with unknown compounds, be aware that certain tests are only useful when the identity of the functional group has been narrowed down to two or fewer.

Some practical advice: You will be performing many tests in test tubes. Be sure that the test tubes are clean, and, for the most part, dry. Most of the tests require that reagents be added in drops. Therefore, most reagents will be distributed in dropper bottles. Be very careful not to contaminate these reagents! Contaminated reagents will give you and your fellow students **false results** and **low grades**. At any given time, there will be many reagents available in the laboratory. *Keep them in order, and do not misuse them. Other students need them, and they are time-consuming to prepare.*

When working with known compounds, always record enough observations in your notebook so that you can remember the results that you obtained from a particular test. This will be especially important when you start working on your unknowns. In addition, if you obtain results which are contrary to those that are expected, you should repeat the test in question. If, after repeating the test, you still obtain the same unexpected result, consult your instructor. It could mean that there is something wrong with one or more of the stock solutions. Make a note of the problem in your notebook.

Finally, since you are going to perform different tests on the same compound, it is advisable to record your results as positive (+) or negative (–) in tabular form and to include short remarks when applicable. Here is an example of such a table for the hydrocarbon test:

Compound Test	Benzene	Naphthalene	Toluene
Conc. H_2SO_4			
Anhy. $AlCl_3$			
Br_2/CH_2Cl_2			
Baeyer			

NOTE: *Students who perform and record the results of their qualitative tests conscientiously do not have trouble with their unknowns.*

Part 1: The Hydrocarbons

The simplest of all classes of organic compounds is the hydrocarbons. These compounds are made up of only carbon and hydrogen atoms, and the bonds in the compound are C–H and either C–C sigma (σ) bonds or C=C pi (π) bonds.

Alkanes are **saturated** hydrocarbons; that is, they have only sigma bonds and cannot add hydrogen. Alkanes are generally very unreactive. They react only with oxygen (referred to as combustion) and with very reactive free radical species.

Alkenes and alkynes are said to be **unsaturated** hydrocarbons because they have at least one π-bond and can add hydrogen. The **double** bond of alkenes consists of one σ-bond and one π-bond between the same two carbon atoms. Alkynes are characterized by the presence of a **triple** bond with one σ-bond and two π-bonds between the same two carbon atoms. The most characteristic chemical property of alkenes and alkynes is that they undergo addition reactions by initial attack on the π-bond by an electrophilic species. This type of reaction is often used as a test for the presence of unsaturated hydrocarbons.

Aromatic hydrocarbons are cyclic hydrocarbons that conform to the $(4n+2)\pi$-electron (Hückel's) rule. Aromatic hydrocarbons are nucleophilic in character and undergo substitution reactions with electrophiles.

The various types of hydrocarbons react differently from one another. Some of these differences are easily observed. These reactions are often used as **classification tests** by which unknown compounds can be partially identified. In order to identify an unknown hydrocarbon, the physical constants of the hydrocarbon are necessary in addition to chemical classification tests. Also useful are spectral data such as IR and NMR.

There are no simple chemical methods for distinguishing between internal alkynes (R–C≡C–R) and alkenes, since the π bonds of alkynes undergo the same reactions as the π bond of alkenes. Physical constants and spectral data are the most important clues in making a distinction between the two types of hydrocarbons. The common reactions and classification tests for hydrocarbons are given below, and on the following pages.

A. SOLUBILITY IN CONCENTRATED SULFURIC ACID

1. When treated with concentrated sulfuric acid, alkanes, benzene, monoalkyl- and some dialkylbenzenes undergo no physical or chemical change and remain as an insoluble layer.

2. More reactive compounds such as polyalkylbenzenes, most alkenes, and most alkynes will dissolve in concentrated sulfuric acid. These compounds dissolve because they form sulfonic acids (from aromatic hydrocarbons) or sulfates (from alkenes and alkynes) when exposed to concentrated sulfuric acid. The sulfates and sulfonates that form are higly polar and are therefore *soluble* in this very polar reagent.

Sulfonic acid

$$RHC = CHR \quad + \quad H_2SO_4 \quad \longrightarrow \quad \underset{H}{R\overset{H}{H}C - \overset{\oplus}{C}HR} \quad \xrightarrow{HOSO_3^{\ominus}} \quad \underset{\quad}{R\overset{H}{H}C - \overset{OSO_3H}{C}HR}$$

Sulfate

3. Many alkenes and alkynes undergo polymerization via a carbocation mechanism when treated with concentrated sulfuric acid. Sulfuric acid protonates a molecule of the alkene or alkyne, and the resulting carbocation undergoes electrophilic addition to another molecule of the unsaturated hydrocarbon. Repetition of this process results in the formation of a polymer.

The resulting polymers are *insoluble* in concentrated sulfuric acid, but their formation is accompanied by *heat*, and the solid polymers have a different *physical appearance* from the original hydrocarbon.

B. ANHYDROUS ALUMINUM CHLORIDE IN CHLOROFORM

Aromatic compounds that do not have strong deactivating substituents, such as $-NO_2$ and $-CN$, react with chloroform ($CHCl_3$) in the presence of anhydrous aluminum chloride resulting in a variety of characteristic colors. The aluminum chloride reacts with the chloroform to produce $AlCl_4^-$ and an electrophilic species ($CHCl_2^+$). The $CHCl_2^+$ then reacts with the aromatic compound via successive Friedel-Crafts reactions, resulting in the formation of triarylmethyl cations (Ar_3C^+). These carbocations have characteristic colors that are listed below. Alkyl- and halogen-substituted aromatic rings usually give the same color as the unsubstituted ring system. Aliphatic hydrocarbons give either no color at all or only a light, straw-yellow color.

Color Produced By Various Aromatic Ring Systems	
Aromatic System	**Color**
Benzene	orange to red
Naphthalene	blue
Biphenyl	purple
Anthracene	green
Phenanthrene	purple

C. FIVE PERCENT BROMINE SOLUTION IN METHYLENE CHLORIDE

Methylene chloride (dichloromethane, CH_2Cl_2) is the solvent for this reaction, because it is a good solvent for elemental bromine and a poor solvent for hydrogen bromide. Although this reagent can react with many compounds other than alkenes and alkynes, it is the decolorization of a bromine solution *without* evolution of HBr gas that is deemed to be a positive test for alkenes and alkynes.

The bromination of alkenes and alkynes is an electrophilic addition reaction and takes place by the following mechanism:

$$RHC = CHR \quad + \quad Br-Br \quad \longrightarrow \quad RCH \overset{\overset{Br}{\diagdown \oplus \diagdown}}{\underset{------}{}} CH_2 \quad + \quad Br^{\ominus} \quad \text{(slow)}$$

$$RCH \overset{\overset{Br}{\diagdown \oplus \diagdown}}{\underset{------}{}} CH_2 \quad + \quad Br^{\ominus} \quad \longrightarrow \quad \overset{Br}{\underset{|}{HCR}} - CH_2Br \quad \text{(fast)}$$

The presence of two or more phenyl groups attached to the double bond diminishes the availability of the π electrons to the attacking Br^+, thereby decreasing the stability of the resulting bridged bromonium ion and causing the reaction to be slow. This results in a reaction with bromine that is so slow that the test appears negative. For this reason, compounds such as ArCH=CHAr and $Ar_2C=CAr_2$ give negative results.

D. AQUEOUS POTASSIUM PERMANGANATE SOLUTION—THE BAEYER TEST

Dilute aqueous potassium permanganate solution produces fewer false negative tests with unsaturated compounds than does bromine in CH_2Cl_2. However, because $KMnO_4$ is such a good oxidizing agent, this reagent gives positive tests with any easily oxidized functional group (such as aldehydes). The test is a good complement, however, to the decolorization of bromine, but you must be certain that carbonyl and reactive hydroxyl groups are absent.

$$\underset{\underset{H}{\overset{Ar}{\diagdown}}}{C} = \underset{\underset{Ar}{\overset{H}{\diagup}}}{C} \quad + \quad 4H_2O \quad + \quad 2KMnO_4 \quad \longrightarrow \quad \underset{\underset{Ar}{\overset{OH}{|}}}{HC} - \underset{\underset{OH}{\overset{Ar}{|}}}{CH} \quad + \quad 2KOH \quad + \quad 2MnO_2$$

For example, 1,2-diphenylethylene, cinnamic acid, and 1,2-dibromoethylene all give negative results with Br_2 in CH_2Cl_2 and positive tests with $KMnO_4$.

Experimental Procedures

Tests A, C, and D should be performed on **naphthalene**, **toluene**, **styrene**, and **hexane**, and an alkene such as **2-pentene** or **cyclohexene**. Record the observations for each test in the form of a table in your notebook. **Test B** should be performed on **naphthalene**, **biphenyl**, **anthracene**, and **2-pentene** (or **cyclohexene**). In tabular form, give a summary of the positive or negative results of each test with the compounds tested.

A. Concentrated H₂SO₄ Test

NOTE: *Handle concentrated sulfuric with care. Wash hands well after use.*

Into dry test tubes, dissolve 50 mg or 5 drops of the hydrocarbons to be tested in 1 mL of concentrated sulfuric acid. *Remember, you are performing qualitative tests. As long as you take more-or-less the same amount of each reagent, the comparison of results will be valid.* Agitate well with the aid of a stirring rod, and record observations in your notebook.

B. Anhydrous Aluminum Chloride In Chloroform Test

CAUTION: *Anhydrous aluminum chloride is a very strong Lewis acid which reacts rapidly with moisture in the air and violently with water. It is very important that all reagents and test tubes be completely dry. The aluminum chloride should be taken from a bottle kept in a desiccator. The bottle should be kept tightly closed except when the reagent is being removed.*

Into dry test tubes, place a small amount of the hydrocarbons to be tested. Add about 2 mL of chloroform, stir well, and put aside. Into a dry test tube, place a pea-sized portion of **anhydrous** aluminum chloride, and heat the salt with a Bunsen burner until it sublimes onto the walls of the tube. Trickle the chloroform solution of the hydrocarbon down onto the freshly sublimed $AlCl_3$. Note the color of both the solid on the wall and of the solution.

C. Bromine In Methylene Chloride Test

Dissolve or disperse a small amount (4 drops or 0.1 g) of the compound in 1 mL of bromine in CH_2Cl_2, one drop at a time, shaking the tube briefly after each addition. If three or more drops are decolorized, the test is positive. If color persists for a few minutes after the addition of one drop, the test should be considered negative. If small bubbles of gas are observed with a positive test, the presence of HBr gas can be detected using moist pH paper. Both HBr and HCl gases will cause a fog with moist air and can be detected by exhaling gently across the mouth of a test tube containing these gases.

D. Aqueous Potassium Permanganate—The Baeyer Test

Dissolve a small amount of the compound (5 drops or 0.1 g) in 1 mL of $KMnO_4$, one drop at a time. Shake the test tube vigorously after the addition of each drop. If the purple color of the permanganate ion disappears immediately after the addition of two drops of the reagent, the presence of an alkene or alkyne is indicated. Remember, this test should only be performed when the absence of easily oxidizable functional groups is assured. In addition to the disappearance of the purple color, there will usually be a brown precipitate of manganese dioxide (MnO_2). At times, the MnO_2 will remain suspended, and a reddish-brown color will gradually replace the purple color.

THE HYDROCARBONS

Flowchart for Hydrocarbon Identification

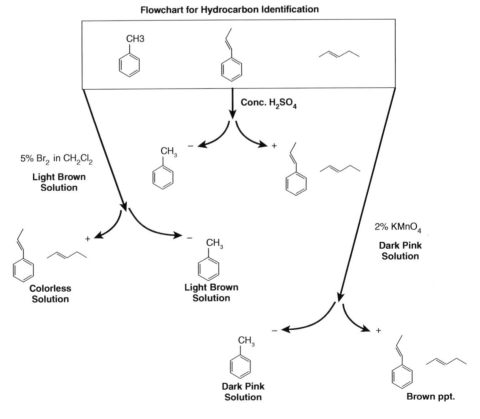

Figure 19-1. *Flowchart for Hydrocarbon Identification.*

Part 2: Alcohols, Phenols, and Ethers

ALCOHOLS

Alcohols are a particularly important class of compounds. The –OH group can react in several ways, and these reactions provide useful routes to other types of functional groups.

The major methods for preparing alcohols are:

1. Acid-catalyzed hydration of alkenes producing secondary and tertiary alcohols,

2. Grignard reaction,

3. Hydroboration-oxidation of alkenes producing primary alcohols,

4. Hydrolysis of alkyl halides, and

5. Reduction of carbonyl compounds.

Alcohols with up to about 14 carbon atoms are liquids with sweet odors. Two major effects caused by the presence the –OH group are the **relatively high boiling point** of alcohols and their **water solubility**. These properties arise from the ability of the –OH group to form intermolecular **hydrogen bonds**. Primary alcohols of 4 carbons or fewer are completely soluble in water, and alcohols of 5–7 carbons are partially soluble in water. When the alcohol is other than secondary or tertiary, water solubility is increased. Cyclic alcohols are also partially soluble in water. The –OH group of alcohols has the ability to react either as an acid or as a base and is therefore **amphoteric**.

The following classification tests are based on the fact that primary alcohols are easily oxidized and that tertiary alcohols rapidly form carbocations. These properties will allow us to distinguish among primary, secondary, and tertiary alcohols.

1. **Ceric Nitrate Test**

   The ceric nitrate test is useful for distinguishing alcohols with less than 10 carbons from alcohols with more than 10 carbons. The ceric ammonium reagent forms a red complex when mixed with primary, secondary, and tertiary alcohols as shown in the following reaction:

$$(NH_4)_2 Ce(NO_3)_6 + ROH \longrightarrow (NH_4)_2 Ce(NO_3)_5 + HNO_3$$

   Yellow

   OR

   Red

Phenols will produce a greenish-brown precipitate when reacted with the reagent. Aromatic amines maybe oxidized by the ceric ammonium nitrate, thereby giving a positive test as well.

2. The Lucas Test

The Lucas test distinguishes among 1°, 2°, and 3° alcohols that have fewer than eight carbon atoms. The test is not used on larger alcohols because of their insolubility in the Lucas reagent.

NOTE: *This test should not be performed if the unknown gives a negative acetyl chloride test (see below).*

The **Lucas test** depends upon the rate of ionization of a protonated alcohol to form a carbocation. The rate of reaction depends upon the stability of the transition state (‡) in the rate-determining step. The presence of zinc chloride assists in the heterolytic cleavage of the C–O bond:

$$\text{ROH} \underset{\text{HCl}}{\overset{\text{ZnCl}_2}{\rightleftharpoons}} \overset{\text{H}}{\underset{\oplus}{R-O-H}} \longrightarrow \left[\overset{\delta+}{R} \text{-------} \overset{\delta+}{\text{OH}_2} \right]^{\ddagger} \longrightarrow \overset{\oplus}{R} + \text{H}_2\text{O}$$

$$\overset{\oplus}{R} + \overset{\ominus}{Cl} \xrightarrow{\text{fast}} \text{RCl}$$

Since the transition state for the first step resembles a carbocation, those structural features that stabilize carbocations also stabilize the transition state and cause an increase in the rate of reaction. The different rates of reaction with the Lucas reagent are used to distinguish among primary, secondary, and tertiary alcohols. Since the order of stability of carbocations is 3°> 2° >1° the reaction rates for the three types of alcohols (1°, 2°, 3°) correspond accordingly.

The visible change indicating that a reaction between the alcohol and the Lucas reagent has taken place is the separation of the insoluble alkyl chloride from the aqueous phase. Tertiary alcohols react almost instantaneously as shown by an immediate white, cloudy suspension. An actual second phase of alkyl chloride separates within 5 minutes. Because of the stability of benzylic and allylic carbocations, alcohols with the structures:

$$\overset{|}{\underset{|}{Ar-C-OH}} \qquad \text{and} \qquad -\overset{|}{C}=\overset{|}{C}-\overset{|}{\underset{|}{C}}-OH$$

give an immediate insoluble chloride just as tertiary alcohols do.

Secondary alcohols produce a milky suspension within five minutes of their addition to the Lucas reagent, and a second phase forms within ten minutes. Primary alcohols (other than the allylic and benzylic type shown above) show no sign of reaction after an hour or longer.

The times for reaction that are given above were measured when the reaction mixture was at room temperature. Carrying out this test at temperatures above or below room temperature causes a marked change in the rate of reaction, especially in the reactions of secondary alcohols. At room temperature, a 10° increase in temperature approximately doubles the rate of this type of reaction.

3. Oxidation with Chromium Trioxide, the Jones Oxidation

Primary and secondary alcohols dissolved in pure acetone readily oxidize with a solution of chromium trioxide in sulfuric acid. This reaction is known as the **Jones oxidation**.

$$3\ RCH_2OH\ +\ 4\ CrO_3\ +\ 12\ H^{\oplus}\ \longrightarrow\ 3\ R-\overset{\overset{\textstyle O}{\|}}{C}-OH\ +\ 4\ Cr^{+3}\ +\ 9H_2O$$

orange   green

$$3\ R_2CHOH\ +\ 2\ CrO_3\ +\ 6\ H^{\oplus}\ \longrightarrow\ 3\ R-\overset{\overset{\textstyle O}{\|}}{C}-R\ +\ 2\ Cr^{+3}\ +\ 6H_2O$$

orange   green

Tertiary alcohols do not oxidize with this reagent because there is no hydrogen on the carbon atom bearing the –OH group. Primary and secondary alcohols react with chromium trioxide in sulfuric acid within three seconds at room temperature to give a green precipitate causing the solution to become opaque, and the initial orange color is replaced by a green color. With tertiary alcohols the solution may become slightly opaque, but it does not turn green at room temperature.

This test can be applied universally to all alcohols, even those of high molecular weight. Carbon–carbon double and triple bonds do not cause cloudiness before 30 seconds, and a green color does not develop until later.

CAUTION: This reaction is also positive with aldehydes. Therefore, their presence must be eliminated before the Jones oxidation can be used as a classification test for alcohols.

4. The Iodoform Test

When the –OH group of an alcohol is located at the second carbon atom of a carbon chain (a so-called **methyl carbinol**), such secondary alcohols can be distinguished from other secondary alcohols with the iodoform test.

$$R-\overset{\overset{\textstyle OH}{|}}{C}H-CH_3\ +\ 3NaOH\ +\ I_2\ \longrightarrow\ R-\overset{\overset{\textstyle O}{\|}}{C}-O^{\ominus}\ +\ CHI_3\ +\ 2NaI\ +\ 2H_2O$$

A methyl carbinol   *Yellow precipitate*

A yellow precipitate of iodoform (CHI_3) indicates a positive test. Occasionally, the iodoform forms an oil instead of a crystalline solid. If so, crystallization can be induced by the usual methods.

NOTE: This reaction is also positive for methyl ketones, acetaldehyde, and ethanol (see later).

5. The Acetyl Chloride Test

Acid halides react readily with the hydroxyl group of alcohols and phenols to form esters and with amines to form amides. This occurs by a nucleophilic attack of oxygen or nitrogen on the electron-deficient carbonyl carbon of the acid halide. Acetyl chloride is the acid chloride most commonly used when performing this classification test.

$$R-OH \ + \ CH_3-\overset{\overset{\displaystyle O}{\|}}{C}-Cl \ \longrightarrow \ CH_3-\overset{\overset{\displaystyle O}{\|}}{C}-OR \ + \ HCl \ + \ Heat$$

Acetyl chloride   *Ester*

When this reaction occurs with alcohols and phenols, heat and the evolution of HCl are detected. The HCl gas can be detected by cautiously exhaling over the mouth of the test tube. This is because hydrogen chloride is soluble in water, and the moist breath of exhalation causes the gas to dissolve to form a fog. The product esters are less dense than water and usually rise to form a layer on top of the reaction mixture. Esters are usually pleasant-smelling liquids whose odor is quite different from that of the original alcohol or phenol.

NOTE: *The acetyl chloride test is also positive for amines except that HCl does not evolve.*

Experimental Procedures

The classification tests described above should be run according to the procedures below. For the alcohol tests use **1-butanol**, **2-butanol**, and **t-butyl** alcohol and compare your results. Record both positive and negative results in the form of a table in your notebook.

1. Ceric Nitrate Test

In a dry test tube, add 50 mg or 5 drops of sample alcohol to be tested. Add 1 mL of the Ceric nitrate reagent (which contains ceric ammonium nitrate dissolved in aqueuous nitric acid). Shake the test tube and observe the results. A red complex should form. If the alcohol sample has low solubility or is water insoluble, the addition of 3–5 drops of diglyme should be added and the solution should be mixed well.

2. The Lucas Test

Into three dry test tubes place 3 drops of each alcohol to be tested, and quickly add 1 mL of the Lucas reagent ($ZnCl_2$ in HCl). Stopper the test tubes, and shake them vigorously but briefly. If the alcohol is not completely soluble in the Lucas reagent, shake the stoppered tube vigorously for 30 seconds. Note the time required both for the appearance of cloudiness and finally for the formation of a distinct second layer. If nothing appears after 25 minutes, record the test as negative and discard the solution.

3. *The Jones Oxidation Test*

Dissolve 1 drop of the alcohol to be tested in 10 drops of *pure, reagent grade acetone*. Add 1 drop of the chromium trioxide reagent to the solution. Shake the tube vigorously for two seconds. Note the time required for any color change or precipitate to form.

4. *The Iodoform Test*

Dissolve a small amount of the compound to be tested in 2 mL of water in a large test tube. If the compound is insoluble in water, add enough 1,2-dimethoxyethane to produce a homogeneous solution. Add 1 mL of 10% NaOH solution. Then add the potassium iodide-iodine (KI/I$_2$) reagent solution *dropwise* with swirling until the dark color of the iodine persists. Allow the mixture to stand for several minutes, and, if no yellow solid (iodoform) precipitates, warm the solution in a water bath maintained at 60°C. If the color disappears, add more of the iodine reagent until the dark color persists for two minutes at 60°C. Add 10% NaOH solution drop by drop with swirling until the dark color disappears, remove the test tube from the water bath, and add 15 mL of water taking care not to overfill the test tube. If the test is positive, the solid iodoform will precipitate at this point.

5. *The Acetyl Chloride Test*

Place 10 drops of the alcohol to be tested in a clean, *dry* test tube, and carefully add 10 drops of acetyl chloride.

CAUTION: *Acetyl chloride reacts vigorously with moisture. Do this test in the hood.*

Mix the reagents thoroughly and note any heat or the evolution of gas. Allow the mixture to stand for at least two minutes, and then add a few small pieces of ice (about the equivalent of 2 mL), and stir the mixture thoroughly. An ester layer should rise to the top of the aqueous phase. Be careful when attempting to smell the product. A good method for comparing odors is to place a drop or two of the compound on a clean, dry piece of filter paper and waft the odors to your nose by fanning the impregnated paper toward your face.

PHENOLS

Phenols are weakly acidic compounds (pK$_a$ ~10) compared to carboxylic acids (pK$_a$ ~5). A positive solubility test in dilute aqueous sodium hydroxide and a negative solubility test in dilute sodium bicarbonate are indicative of a phenol.

There are two color tests which can be used to classify an unknown as a phenol: the **ceric nitrate test** and the **ferric chloride test**. Each of these is a color test, and care must be taken to perform such tests not only on the unknown compound but on a blank as well. This is because it is very easy to mistake the diluted color of the reagent for a positive test.

The **acetyl chloride test** yields the ester of a phenol just as it does with alcohols. This test is performed in the same way as described in the section on alcohols.

The **bromination test** is not specifically aimed at the –OH group, but rather treats the aromatic ring as a functional group (the –OH group is a very strong ring activator so that the aromatic ring of phenol brominates quite readily).

1. **The Ceric Nitrate Test, Ce(NO$_3$)$_4$**

   A positive ceric nitrate test for phenols is a brown to greenish-brown precipitate in aqueous solution for those phenols that are water soluble. Water-insoluble phenols afford a red to brown solution in the solvent dioxane or diglyme.

   NOTE: Be cautious when dealing with water-insoluble compounds; alcohols may also give a red color with this test. For this reason, it is wise to perform the ferric chloride test as well for confirmation (see below).

2. **The Ferric Chloride Test, FeCl$_3$**

   Most phenols produce intense red, blue, purple, or green colorations with this test. However, not all phenols produce color with this reagent. One should run a blank along with the known compound because the color produced may not be permanent, and observations should be taken as close together as possible.

3. **The Acetyl Chloride Test**

   See the discussion under the alcohols, Test #4.

   CAUTION: This test is also positive for the amino group but without the evolution of HCl gas.

4. **The Bromination of Phenols**

   A solution of bromine in water is decolorized by phenols. Once the presence of the –OH group has been established, this test is useful in distinguishing alcohols from phenols and complements the ceric nitrate and ferric chloride color tests. In addition to the decolorization of bromine water, a solid may precipitate.

   CAUTION: Some other aromatic compounds may also cause the decoloration of bromine water.

Experimental Procedures

The tests below should be performed on **phenol** and **p-nitrophenol**. Record both positive and negative results in the form of a table in your lab notebook.

CAUTION: Be very careful when handling phenols; they burn the skin badly! If they come in contact with your skin, wash it immediately with plenty of water.

1. **The Solubility Test**

   Place a small amount of the compound in a small test tube, and test its solubility in water, 5% sodium hydroxide, and 5% sodium bicarbonate. Use 3 mL of each solvent and stir each mixture well. *Under no circumstances should test tubes be heated to induce solution.* If the phenol is soluble in water, test the pH of the resulting aqueous solution with pH paper and record the results. If phenol is water insoluble, the addition of 1 mL of diglyme should be used for the ceric nitrate test, ferric chloride test, acetyl chloride test, and bromine water test.

2. **The Ceric Nitrate Test**

   Dissolve a small amount of the phenol in 1 mL of water. Add 5 drops of this solution to about 1 mL of ceric nitrate reagent diluted with 3 mL of water. If the solution decolorizes, add additional $Ce(NO_3)_4$ reagent until the solution remains yellow or it changes color.

3. **The Ferric Chloride Test**

   Dissolve a small amount of the phenol in 1 mL of water, and add 3 drops of the ferric chloride solution.

4. **The Acetyl Chloride Test**

   See Alcohol Tests Procedure.

5. **The Bromine Water Test**

   Dissolve three drops or 0.1 g of the compound in 10 mL of water. If the compound is insoluble, add ethanol dropwise to bring it into solution. Add bromine water dropwise until a yellow-orange color persists. If more than 3–4 drops of bromine water are required to cause color, add an additional 10 mL of water to the test solution, and check for the formation of a pale yellow to off-white solid (the tribromophenol).

ETHERS

The chemistry of ethers focuses on the oxygen atom. The ether oxygen can be protonated to form an oxonium ion and, therefore, ethers will dissolve in very strong acid.

$$R—\overset{\cdot\cdot}{\underset{\cdot\cdot}{O}}—R' \quad + \quad H^+ \quad \rightleftharpoons \quad R—\underset{\underset{\oplus}{\cdot\cdot}}{\overset{\overset{H}{|}}{O}}—R'$$

An oxonium
ion

The primary evidence for the presence of an ether is usually found by taking an infrared spectrum of the unknown. Ethers are only a little more polar than saturated hydrocarbons and are chemically unreactive. Aromatic ethers may be identified through derivatization of the aromatic ring *via* nitration or bromination, but aliphatic ethers are difficult to identify.

Part 3: Aldehydes and Ketones

According to resonance theory, the carbonyl group of aldehydes and ketones can be described as a hybrid of resonance structures I and II.

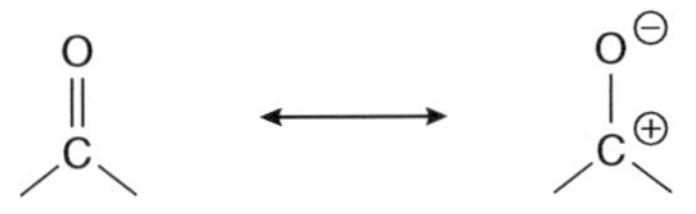

It is the contribution of resonance structure II that causes the carbonyl group to be polar. A consequence of this is that aldehydes and ketones are polar compounds. The resulting electrostatic attraction between molecules results in higher boiling points for aldehydes and ketones than for alkanes of comparable molecular weight.

Many naturally occurring compounds contain the aldehyde or ketone functional group. Aldehydes are the principal constituents of many essential oils that are used as fragrances and flavors such as lemon, hyacinth, and cinnamon.

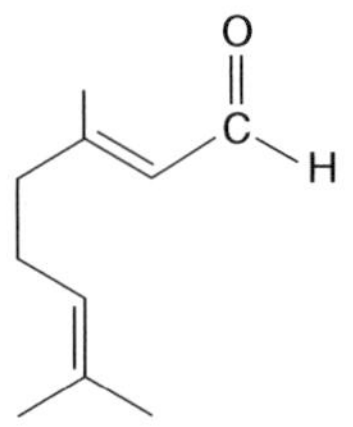

Citral
(Lemon oil)

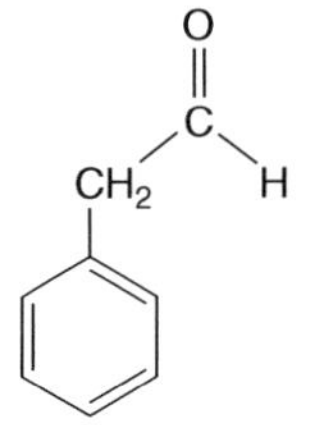

Hyacinthal
(Hyacinth)

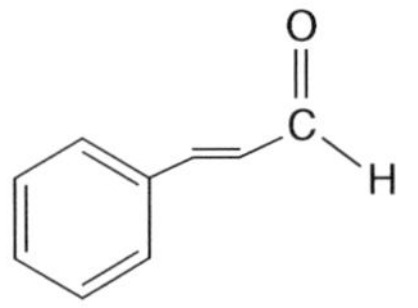

Cinnamaldehyde
(Cinnamon)

Examples of ketones that are found in nature are camphor, which is found in pine oil, menthone, which is found in mint, and carvone, which comes from caraway oil.

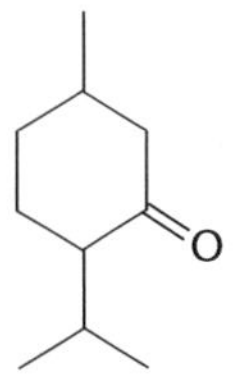

Menthone

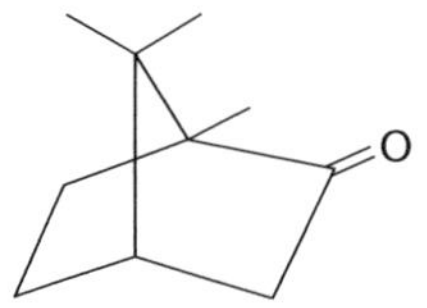

Camphor

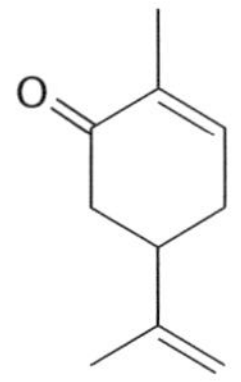

Carvone

The aldehyde group is present in most sugars, and many steroidal hormones are complex cyclic ketones.

The most common reaction of aldehydes and ketones is nucleophilic addition. The carbonyl carbon atom is electron-deficient and susceptible to attack by electron-rich reagents (nucleophiles).

Aldehydes and ketones react with ammonia and its derivatives to give products which are generally solid, crystalline substances and therefore make very useful derivatives. The following have been found to be the most useful derivatives for isolation and subsequent identification of aldehydes and ketones:

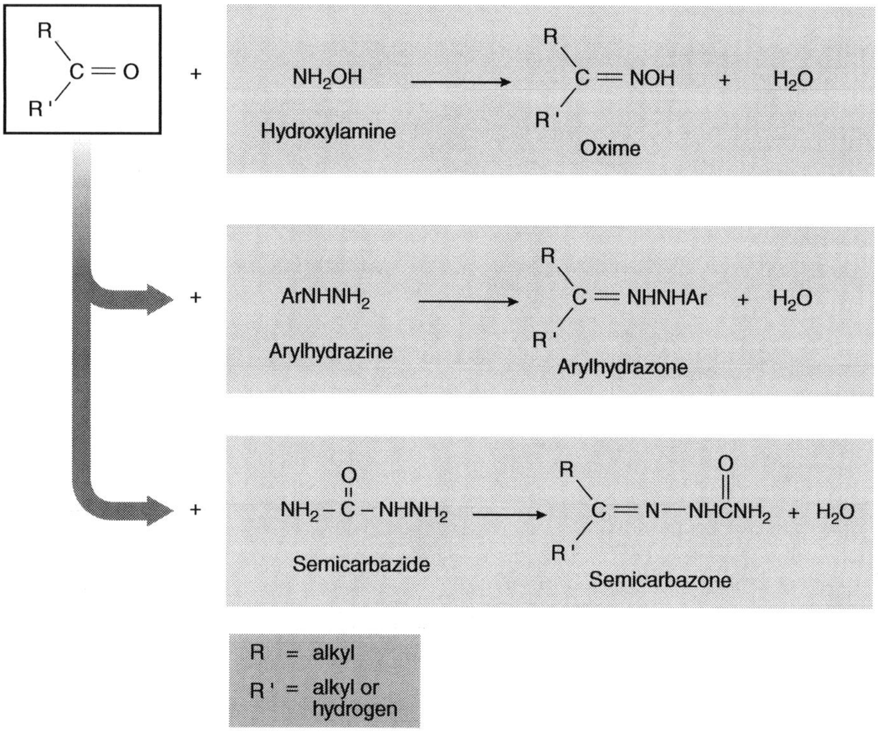

Below are some of the common reactions of aldehydes and ketones that are used as **classification tests** of these two functional groups.

1. Reaction with Arylhydrazines

Of the several ammonia derivatives, phenylhydrazine and 2,4-dinitrophenylhydrazine are the most widely used as reliable tests for aldehydes and ketones. Any compound suspected of being an aldehyde or ketone should therefore be tested with one of these reagents. For water-soluble aldehydes and ketones, 2,4-dinitrophenylhydrazones are the preferred derivatives.

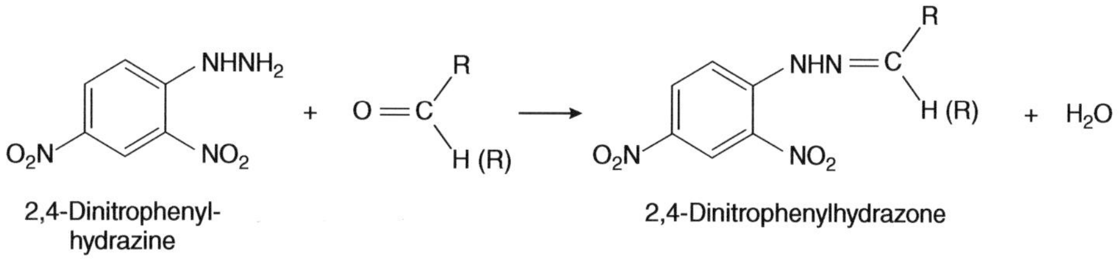

2. Tollens Test

Because it is a very weak oxidizing agent, reaction with silver ion provides a very specific test for the presence of aldehydes. The Tollens test can therefore be used to differentiate between aldehydes and ketones. Tollens' reagent, which is silver ion as its ammonia complex in aqueous base, is used for this purpose. Aldehydes will usually reduce silver ion to yield a precipitate of silver metal which appears as a mirror on the test tube wall.

$$R-C(=O)-H + 2[Ag(NH_3)_2]OH \longrightarrow R-C(=O)-O^{\ominus} + NH_4^+ + 3NH_3 + 2Ag^0 + H_2O$$

The Tollens test should be done *on all compounds that produce a precipitate with the arylhydrazines.*

3. The Iodoform Test

This test is specific for methyl ketones. A yellow precipitate of iodoform, CHI_3, indicates the presence of one of these kinds of compounds.

$$R-C(=O)-CH_3 + 4NaOH + 3I_2 \longrightarrow R-C(=O)-O^{\ominus} + CHI_3 + H_2O$$
Yellow

Acetaldehyde, ethanol and methylcarbinols (2° alcohols with at least one methyl group attached to the carbinol carbon) are other compounds that will undergo this reaction. Therefore, this test should be used only if it has already been determined that the unknown compound is either an aldehyde or a ketone.

4. The Chromic Acid Test

Another way to distinguish between aldehydes and ketones involves the oxidation of the aldehyde by chromic acid. In this reaction, chromic acid is reduced to Cr(III), and the color of the mixture changes from orange to green. Ketones are not oxidized by chromic acid, so they do not undergo this reaction. While this test complements the Tollens test, it is also useful because it can distinguish between aliphatic and aromatic aldehydes based upon how long it takes for the color change to occur.

$$2\,CrO_3 \;+\; 2\,H_2O \;\xrightarrow{\;H^+\;}\; 2\,H_2CrO_4 \;\xrightarrow{\;H^+\;}\; H_2Cr_2O_7 \;+\; H_2O$$

Chromic acid (yellow)   Dichromic acid (orange)

$$3 \underset{\substack{R\quad H\\ \text{Aldehyde}}}{\overset{O}{C}} \;+\; H_2Cr_2O_7 \;+\; 3\,H_2SO_4 \longrightarrow 3 \underset{\substack{R\quad OH\\ \text{Carboxylic acid}}}{\overset{O}{C}} \;+\; Cr_2(SO_4)_3{\downarrow} \;+\; 4\,H_2O$$

Dichromic acid (orange)   Green precipitate

$$\underset{\substack{R\quad R'\\ \text{Ketone}}}{\overset{O}{C}} \;+\; H_2Cr_2O_7 \;+\; 3\,H_2SO_4 \longrightarrow \text{No reaction}$$

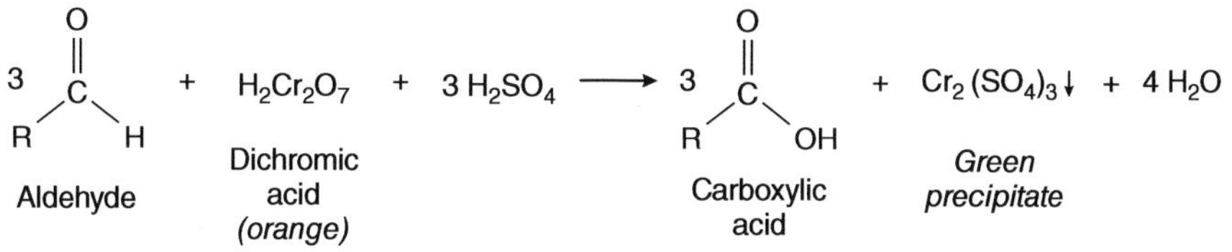

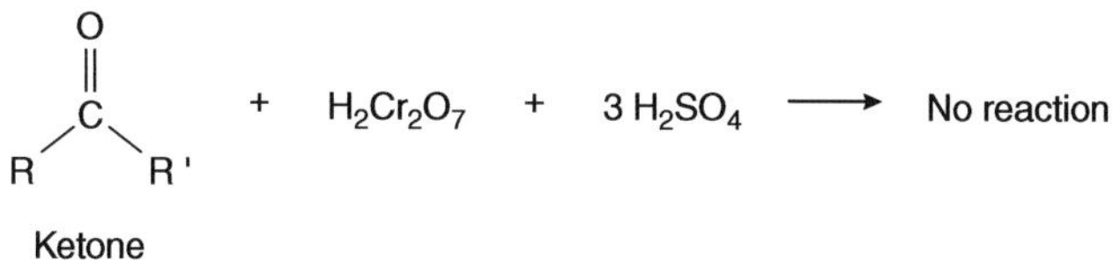

Primary and secondary alcohols will also give a positive test, but in less time. Therefore, one should be fairly certain that the unknown is actually an aldehyde or a ketone before performing this test, to avoid possible confusion. For example, aldehydes and ketones give a positive 2,4-dinitrophenylhydrazine test, while alcohols do not.

5. Schiff's Test

Schiff's test is an additional experiment to distinguish between aldehydes and ketones. The Schiff reagent can react with an aldehyde to form a complex that is magenta in color. The test is not necessary if previous tests have already distinguished the two; however, if inconsistencies in experimental data occur, this test can be used to verify the presence or absence of an aldehyde.

Experimental Procedures

Examine the behavior of four carbonyl compounds: **cyclohexanone, acetone, acetophenone,** and **butyraldehyde**. Report the results of your tests in the form of a table in your lab notebook.

CAUTION: You should not routinely rinse your test tubes with acetone while performing these tests. Acetone is a methyl ketone, and its presence as a contaminant may mask the distinctive results of the test compounds.

1. ***The 2,4-Dinitrophenylhydrazine Test***

    Place a small amount of the solid or liquid to be tested into a small test tube (if it is solid add sufficient ethanol to dissolve the compound). Add about 1 mL of the 2,4-dinitrophenylhydrazine reagent to the test tube, and shake vigorously. The solution should be allowed to stand for 15 minutes if a precipitate does not form immediately. The formation of a yellow to orange or even red precipitate is a positive test.

    NOTE: Any solid produced in this test can be collected and used as a derivative for further identification by recrystallizing it from ethanol or an ethanol–water mixture and taking its melting point.

2. ***Tollens Test***

    Thoroughly scrub and rinse a test tube. Add 2 mL of 5% aqueous silver nitrate and one drop of 10% aqueous sodium hydroxide. Add dropwise with shaking 2 M aqueous ammonium hydroxide until the dark Ag_2O precipitate just dissolves. Add a matchhead-size portion of the solid or one drop of the liquid unknown, and agitate the test tube well to mix the chemicals. Allow the mixture to sit at room temperature for 15 minutes. If no silver mirror is formed on the wall of the test tube, warm the mixture in a 35–40° water bath for a few minutes. Be careful not to shake the tube or stir the contents after the initial mixing. A mirror on the wall of the test tube is positive for an aldehyde. A dense black precipitate may form, and this is also a positive test. A few tiny black flakes or specks, however, should be ignored.

    NOTE: Tollens reagent, upon standing, has the capability of forming silver fulminate ($AgC_2N_2O_2$), a violently explosive compound. Therefore, prepare Tollens reagent immediately before use, and dispose of the test solutions immediately after use by flushing them down the drain with plenty of water.

3. ***The Iodoform Test***

    In a large test tube, dissolve a small amount of the compound to be tested (5 drops of liquid or about 100 mg of solid) in 2 mL of water. If the compound is insoluble in water, add enough 1,2-dimethoxyethane to produce a homogeneous solution. Add 1 mL of 10% NaOH solution and the potassium iodide-iodine (KI/I_2) reagent *dropwise* with stirring until the dark color of the iodine persists. Allow the mixture to stand for several minutes. If no yellow solid (iodoform) precipitates, warm the solution in a water bath maintained at 60°C. If the color disappears, add more of the iodine reagent until the dark color persists for two minutes while at 60°C. Add 10% NaOH solution drop by drop with stirring until the dark color disappears, remove the test tube from the water bath, and add 15 mL of water taking care not to overfill the test tube. If the test is positive, then solid iodoform will precipitate at this point.

4. *Chromic Acid Test*

Check the reagent grade acetone for purity by adding 5 drops of chromic acid to 10 drops of acetone. If no green precipitate forms within 3 to 5 minutes, then the acetone is pure enough to use as the solvent for this test.

Dissolve 2 drops of liquid sample or about 15 mg of a solid sample in 20 drops of pure acetone. Add 5 drops of chromic acid, 1 drop at a time, to the acetone solution with agitation. Observe how long it takes for any green precipitate to form. With aliphatic aldehydes, the precipitate usually appears within 30 seconds, but with aromatic aldehydes it usually takes from 30 seconds to over two minutes.

5. *Schiff's test*

In a dry test tube, add 50 mg or 5 drops of sample aldehyde/ketone to be tested. Add 1 mL of the Schiff's reagent. Shake the test tube and observe the results. A magenta color complex will form in the presence of an aldehyde.

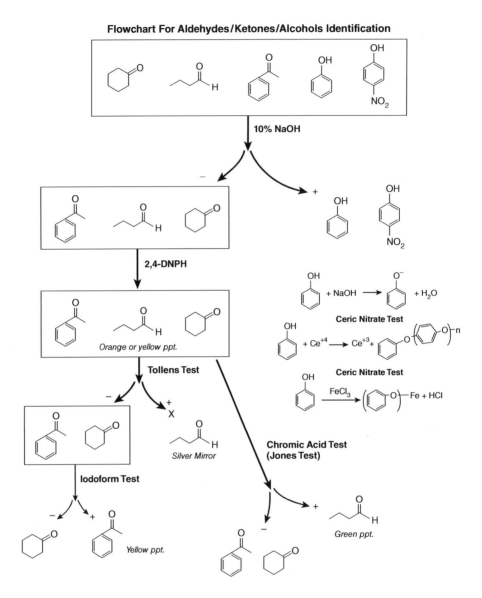

Figure 19-2. *Flowchart for Aldehydes/Ketones/Alcohols Identification.*

IDENTIFICATION OF AN UNKNOWN ALDEHYDE OR KETONE

Although modern chemists rely heavily on instrumental analytical methods, there are a host of "wet" chemical tests for identifying functional groups. Once the type of molecule is known, a solid derivative of the original compound can be prepared, and its melting point compared to those of known compounds. If several known derivatives have similar melting points, a second or even a third derivative may have to be prepared. The odds of two different compounds having two or three derivatives with the same melting points are very small; thus, the unknown can usually be identified.

In this experiment, each student will receive a sample of an unknown aldehyde or ketone. By preparing at least two solid derivatives of the unknown, purifying them, and comparing the melting points with those listed in the table at the end of this experiment, the student should be able to identify the unknown. As an additional aid, a chemical test for distinguishing between aldehydes and ketones is described and may be utilized if needed. No instrumental methods of analysis will be used in this experiment.

A. General Procedure

1. Secure a sample of your unknown. Make sure to record the ID number of the unknown in your notebook.

2. Read the "Review of Recrystallization," which is given at the end of this experiment.

3. The easiest derivative to prepare is usually the 2,4-dinitrophenylhydrazone (2,4-DNPH). Following Procedure B, prepare the 2,4-DNPH derivative of your unknown. Dry the solid, and determine its melting point.

    NOTE: *The solid may be recrystallized from ethanol or from an ethanol and water mixture.*

4. While the first derivative is drying, prepare a second derivative, the semicarbazone. Dry this solid, and take its melting point.

    NOTE: *The semicarbazone derivative may also be recrystallized from ethanol or ethanol/water.*

5. Since you know that your unknown is either an aldehyde or a ketone, you should now carry out the chromic acid test as described in Part D in order to distinguish between these two functional groups.

6. Compare the melting points of your derivatives with those in the table on page 177.

    REMEMBER: *An impure compound may melt at a lower temperature than the literature value, but not higher.*

7. Your melting point data—combined with the results from the chromic acid test—should allow you to decide on the identity of your unknown.

If you have time, you might also want to determine the boiling point (or melting point) range of your unknown aldehyde or ketone. This additional physical constant will help to confirm the identity of your unknown.

8. When you have identified your unknown, turn in your results and your solid derivatives. The results should include all of the information concerning your unknown, including the experimental melting points, the values from the table on page 177, additional test results, and so forth.

B. Preparation of a 2,4-Dinitrophenylhydrazone

2, 4–Dinitrophenylhydrazine

a 2, 4–Dinitrophenylhydrazone

1. Add approximately 0.5 g of the unknown aldehyde or ketone to 20 mL of freshly prepared 2,4-dinitrophenylhydrazine solution and mix. If the unknown is a solid, dissolve it first in the minimum amount of 95% ethanol.

    CAUTION: *2,4-Dinitrophenylhydrazine is toxic, and its derivatives may be carcinogenic. Avoid skin contact. Wash hands thoroughly after using.*

2. Allow the resulting mixture to stand at room temperature for 15 minutes if an immediate precipitate is not formed. If necessary, heat the solution gently for one minute, and allow it to stand for another 15 minutes.

3. Cool the reaction mixture in an ice bath to maximize crystallization, and vacuum filter the solid. Use a Hirsch funnel, rather than a Büchner funnel, if it is available.

4. Recrystallization can usually be effected in the following manner: The 2,4-dinitrophenylhydrazone is heated on a hot water bath in 95% ethanol. If solution occurs immediately, water is added slowly until the cloudy point is reached or until a maximum of 5 mL of water has been added. If the 2,4-dinitrophenylhydrazone does not dissolve, ethyl acetate is added slowly to the hot mixture until solution is attained. The hot solution is filtered through a fluted filter and the allowed to stand at room temperature until crystallization is completed. The crystals are then collected by vacuum filtration.

5. Dry the solid and determine its melting point.

C. Preparation of a Semicarbazone

$$H_2N - \overset{\overset{\displaystyle O}{\|}}{C} - NHNH_2 \quad + \quad O = C\overset{\displaystyle R}{\underset{\displaystyle H \,(R)}{}} \quad \longrightarrow$$

Semicarbazide

$$H_2N - \overset{\overset{\displaystyle O}{\|}}{C} - \overset{\overset{\displaystyle H}{}}{N} - N = C\overset{\displaystyle R}{\underset{\displaystyle H \,(R)}{}} \quad + \quad H_2O$$

A semicarbazone

1. Prepare the semicarbazide reagent by dissolving 1 g of semicarbazide hydrochloride and 1.5 g of sodium acetate in 10 mL of water in a 6-inch test tube.

    CAUTION: *Semicarbazide is toxic. Avoid contact with skin or clothing.*

2. In another small test tube, dissolve 1 mL of a liquid unknown or 1 g of a solid unknown in the minimum amount of 95% ethanol. Add this solution to the semi-carbazide hydrochloride solution.

3. Heat the tube (unstoppered) in a boiling water bath for five minutes.

4. Cool the tube in an ice water bath for 5–10 minutes to facilitate crystallization. If no crystals form, scratch the inside of the tube with a glass rod.

5. When crystallization is complete, vacuum filter the product, and rinse with 5 mL of ice water.

6. Recrystallize the product from ethanol or an ethanol/water mixture. The filtrate should be placed in the waste solvent container for disposal.

THE PURIFICATION OF SOLIDS (A REVIEW)

Theory of Recrystallization

The first step in the purification of an organic solid is to dissolve it in a suitable solvent. The impurities contained in the solid may be of two types: (1) impurities which are *insoluble* in the chosen solvent, and (2) impurities which are *soluble* in the chosen solvent. These two types of impurities can be removed as follows:

Insoluble Impurities: Insoluble impurities are usually removed by simple gravity filtration. The solution is usually kept hot during the filtration to prevent the compound being purified from crystallizing out and remaining on the filter paper along with the insoluble impurities.

Soluble Impurities: Once any insoluble impurities have been removed, the clear solution that remains contains the compound of interest along with any soluble impurities. These soluble impurities can now be removed by *recrystallization*. If the correct amount of solvent has been used, there will be just enough solvent to create a solution that is saturated with the compound to be purified when the solution is boiling. If there is excess solvent, some of it should be boiled off before beginning the cooling process. The saturated solution of the compound of interest in the boiling solvent is then allowed to cool slowly. As cooling proceeds, the solution will become supersaturated, and the compound will begin to precipitate (*i.e.*, crystallize out). Since any soluble impurities are normally present in only small amounts, there will not be enough of them to saturate the solution even when it is chilled. Therefore, the impurities will remain in the solution and can be discarded with the solvent after the recrystallized compound has been removed by vacuum filtration.

Recrystallization may be carried out in a single solvent or in a mixed solvent pair. A description of these two techniques follows.

Technique of Recrystallization

Single Solvent: The compound to be purified must be very soluble in the hot solvent and fairly insoluble in cold solvent.

1. Place the compound in a suitable container (usually an Erlenmeyer flask or test tube), and add the boiling solvent in small amounts with stirring until the solid just dissolves.

2. Allow the container to cool to room temperature, and finally chill it in an ice bath to increase the amount of material recovered.

3. Collect the purified product by vacuum filtration (filter flask and Büchner or Hirsch funnel), and rinse the crystals with *a small amount* of *chilled* solvent to remove any impurities which might have remained on the surface of the crystals.

Mixed Solvents: The compound to be purified must be very soluble in one solvent and only sparingly soluble in the other.

1. Boil the solvent in which the compound is very soluble and dissolve the crystals in a minimum amount of this solvent as described above.

2. Keep this solution hot, and add to it *very small amounts* of the boiling solvent in which the compound is only sparingly soluble until cloudiness appears.

3. Add a small amount of the first solvent (boiling) until the solution is just clear. The hot solution using the mixed solvents should now be saturated.

4. Cool the solution, and proceed as with a single solvent. (Rinse the crystals with the poor solvent).

Table of Aldehyde and Ketone Derivatives

Compounds are listed in order of increasing melting point of the 2,4-DNPH derivative				
#	Name of Compound	b.p. (m.p.)	Semi-carbazone	2,4-Dinitro-phenyl-hydrazone	Chromic Acid Test
1	α-Naphthaldehyde	292 (34 m.p.)	221	oil	(+) slow
2	3-Hexanone	125	113	oil	(–)
3	Diisopropyl ketone	125	160	95	(–)
4	Dibenzyl ketone	330 (34 m.p.)	146	100	(–)
5	*n*-Butyl methyl ketone	129	122	106	(–)
6	Octaldehyde	171	101	106	(+)
7	Phenylacetaldehyde	194	156	121	(+)
8	Methyl ethyl ketone	80	146	117	(–)
9	*n*-Butyraldehyde	74	104	122	(+)
10	Pinacolone	106	157	125	(–)
11	Acetone	56	187	126	(–)
12	Cyclohexyl methyl ketone	180	177	140	(–)
13	Cyclopentanone	131	205	142	(–)
14	Methyl *n*-propyl ketone	102	110	144	(–)
15	Menthone	207	187	146	(–)
16	Hydrocinnamaldehyde	224	127	149	(+)
17	Diethyl ketone	102	139	156	(–)
18	Cyclohexanone	155	166	162	(–)
19	Isobutyrophenone	222	181	163	(–)
20	Acrolein	52	171	165	(+)
21	Isobutyraldehyde	64	125	182	(+)
22	Crotonaldehyde	103	199	190	(+)
23	Propiophenone	218	174	191	(–)
24	*o*-Tolualdehyde	200	208	195	(+) slow
25	Methyl *m*-Tolyl Ketone	220	200	207	(–)
26	Pivaldehyde	75	190	209	(+)
27	*m*-Tolualdehyde	199	213	211	(+) slow
28	*p*-Methoxyacetophenone	(38 m.p.)	198	220	(–)
29	*m*-Nitroacetophenone	(81 m.p.)	257	228	(–)
30	Furfural	161	202	229	(+) slow
31	Benzaldehyde	179	222	237	(+) slow
32	Benzophenone	(48 m.p.)	164	239	(–)
33	Acetophenone	200	198	250	(–)
34	Salicylaldehyde	196	231	252d	(+) slow
35	3,4-Dimethoxybenzaldehyde	(44 m.p.)	177	265	(+) slow
36	*p*-Chlorobenzaldehyde	(47 m.p.)	230	270	(+) slow
37	Fluorenone	(83 m.p.)	234	283	(–)
38	*m*-Nitrobenzaldehyde	(58 m.p.)	246	293d	(+) slow

Part 4: Amines and Nitro Compounds

AMINES

The acid/base properties of primary and secondary amines parallel those of ammonia. Amines are the bases of organic chemistry because of the readily-available unshared electron pair on nitrogen. Amines as a functional group, therefore, are usually detected by their basic properties.

Primary (RNH_2), secondary (R_2NH), and tertiary (R_3N) amines are much stronger bases than water, and an aqueous solution of an amine has an alkaline pH. Amines with five or fewer carbon atoms are generally soluble in water while those with 6 to 10 carbon atoms are only partially soluble in water. None of the aromatic amines is water soluble.

Because of their basicity, almost all amines are soluble in dilute, aqueous hydrochloric acid.

Primary and secondary amines react with benzenesulfonyl chloride in aqueous NaOH. This reaction, called the Hinsberg test, serves as a classification test for amines.

1. The Hinsberg Test (Benzenesulfonyl Chloride and NaOH)

All primary and secondary amines react with benzenesulfonyl chloride to yield N-substituted or N,N-disubstituted benzenesulfonamides. Tertiary amines do not react with sulfonyl chlorides.

The sulfonamides of primary amines have an acidic proton on the nitrogen atom and can therefore be deprotonated by hydroxide ion. On the other hand, sulfonamides derived from secondary amines have no such amido hydrogen and cannot be so deprotonated. They do not, therefore, dissolve in aqueous alkaline solution. This difference between the two types of benzenesulfonamides serves as a basis to distinguish between primary and secondary amines.

The precipitate that forms from the Hinsberg test is checked for solubility in 5% hydrochloric acid to aid in distinguishing tertiary amines from precipitated sulfonamides (a tertiary amine will dissolve in 5% HCl while a sulfonamide will not).

If no solid precipitates in the Hinsberg test, the reaction mixture is acidified to determine if an N-monosubstituted benzenesulfonamide or a water-soluble tertiary amine is present. Precipitation of a solid indicates an N-monosubstituted benzenesulfonamide leading to the conclusion that the original unknown is a primary amine.

$$RNH_2 \;+\; \langle\text{benzene}\rangle\text{–}SO_2Cl \;+\; 2\,\overset{\ominus}{O}H \longrightarrow \langle\text{benzene}\rangle\text{–}SO_2\overset{\ominus}{N}R \;+\; Cl^{\ominus} \;+\; 2\,H_2O$$

1° Amine   Benzene-sulfonyl chloride   Soluble product

$$R_2NH \;+\; \langle\text{benzene}\rangle\text{–}SO_2Cl \;+\; \overset{\ominus}{O}H \longrightarrow \langle\text{benzene}\rangle\text{–}SO_2NR_2 \;+\; Cl^{\ominus} \;+\; 2\,H_2O$$

2° Amine   Benzene-sulfonyl chloride   Solid, insoluble product

$$R_3N \;+\; \langle\text{benzene}\rangle\text{–}SO_2Cl \;+\; \overset{\ominus}{O}H \longrightarrow \text{No reaction (heterogenous mixture)}$$

3° Amine   Benzene-sulfonyl chloride

The principal *exceptions* found in the Hinsberg test are the higher molecular weight cyclic amines, beginning with cyclohexylamine, and highly branched aliphatic amines such as 2-amino-2,4,4-trimethylpentane. This exception should be noted since one of the amines to be tested will be cyclohexylamine.

When performing a Hinsberg test, it is useful to note whether any water-insoluble material that forms from the reaction floats or sinks. Tertiary amines are usually less dense than the 10% sodium hydroxide solution used for the test, while all sulfonamides are much denser. Such observations should be interpreted carefully, however, since the presence of halogen atoms in the amine may affect the density such that a tertiary amine may, in fact, be more dense than water and therefore sink. Interpretation of this test can be sometimes be tricky.

When a precipitate is obtained from the Hinsberg test, it should be recrystallized, dried, and the melting point determined so that the benzenesulfonamide can serve as a derivative of the unknown. Often, only the melting point of the benzenesulfonamide, the physical properties of the amine, and the results of one or two other classification tests are needed to identify a primary or secondary amine. Other arenesulfonyl chlorides, however, are also used to obtain arenesulfonamide derivatives of amines.

2. The Acetyl Chloride Test

Review the discussion of this reaction in the section on Alcohols, Phenols, and Ethers.

Unlike the reaction of acetyl chloride with alcohols or phenols, HCl gas is *not* evolved when the reagent is added to amines. For example, in the reaction of acetyl chloride with aniline:

a second molecule of amine reacts with the HCl that is formed, such that no gas evolution occurs. Heat, however, is evolved when acetyl chloride is added to an amine, and dilution of the reaction mixture with ice water results in the precipitation of an acetamide. No solid forms in the case of tertiary amines, since the only reaction is salt formation:

Experimental Procedures

The following tests should be performed on **N,N-dimethylaniline, N-methylaniline, 2-aminobutane (*sec*-butylamine)**, and **cyclohexylamine**. Record the results as positive or negative in the form of a table in your laboratory notebook. Be sure that you record two sets of observations for the Hinsberg test: (1) the initial reaction in basic solution and the results of acidification, and (2) the three sets of results in the solubility test. Remember that the Hinsberg test on cyclohexylamine is an exception. Make careful observations. Save any precipitates from the Hinsberg test, and take the melting points for comparison with the literature values.

1. ***The Solubility Test***

   Test the solubility of the amines in 5 mL of water, 5 mL of 5% hydrochloric acid, and 5 mL of 5% aqueous sodium hydroxide by adding about two drops of the amine. If the amine dissolves in water, test the solution with pH paper and record the result; then omit the tests with sodium hydroxide and hydrochloric acid. (Why?)

2. ***The Hinsberg Test***

   CAUTION: *Arenesulfonyl chlorides are lachrymators. Perform this test **in the hood**.*

   Wear rubber gloves; benzenesulfonyl chloride and amines are corrosive/caustic.

   Put 5 mL of 10% potassium hydroxide, 0.2 g of a solid or 0.2 mL of a liquid unknown, and 0.7 mL of benzenesulfonyl chloride in a test tube. Stopper the tube tightly, and shake it vigorously over a period of five minutes, cooling the mixture if necessary to kept it at about room temperature. Test the solution after five minutes to see if it is basic. If not, add 10% aqueous KOH dropwise with shaking until it is basic.

   If a precipitate or a second liquid phase forms, make a note of the relative densities of the two phases, and then separate the phases by filtering, decanting, or withdrawing with Pasteur pipet. Add dropwise with shaking 10% hydrochloric acid to the organic phase, and observe whether the organic phase goes into solution. If not, the unknown is probably a secondary amine; if it does, it is probably a tertiary amine. If, after the 5-minute shaking period of the original reaction mixture there is no second phase, the unknown is probably a primary amine. Acidify the mixture to pH 4 with 10% hydrochloric acid. The presence of a primary amine is confirmed by separation of a precipitate or a second liquid layer.

NOTE: *The arenesulfonamides made from aliphatic and aromatic amines usually serve as good crystalline derivatives. If the benzenesulfonamide is a solid, recrystallize it and use it as a derivative. If the benzenesulfonamide is a liquid, another arenesulfonyl chloride such as p-toluenesulfonyl chloride, p-nitrobenzenesulfonyl chloride, or p-bromobenzenesulfonyl chloride may be used instead.*

3. The Acetyl Chloride Test (optional)

See the discussion and test procedures in the section on alcohols. In this test, one looks particularly for a lack of gas (HCl) evolution and the formation of a solid product. If a solid does form, it should be collected by vacuum filtration, washed with water, dried, and a melting point taken for comparison with the literature values of the acetamide derivatives of amines.

$$2\ R-NH_2 \text{ or } 2\ R_2NH + CH_3-\overset{\overset{O}{\|}}{C}-Cl \longrightarrow CH_3-\overset{\overset{O}{\|}}{C}-\underset{-NR_2}{NHR} + \overset{\oplus}{RNH_3}\overset{\ominus}{Cl} \text{ or } \overset{\oplus}{R_2NH_2}\overset{\ominus}{Cl}$$

Acetyl chloride → Acetamide derivative

Amine Derivatives

The most common derivatives made with amines are the benzensulfonamides, benzamides, and *p*-toluenesulfonamides. Procedures for preparing such derivatives are found in pages 198–200. Using the same approach taken for making aldehydes/ketone derivatives, prepare one amine derivative with your unknown amine and take the melting point of compound. Using your data from the Hinsburg test and comparing the melting point of our derivative with the melting point of known derivatives (pages 217–222), identify your unknown amine.

NITRO COMPOUNDS

Nitro compounds are most easily identified by infrared spectroscopy. Elemental analysis for the presence of nitrogen should also be used.

The presence of a nitro group on an aromatic ring can often be inferred by the yellow color imparted by this group. Nitrobenzene, for example, is pale yellow, the nitroanilines are bright yellow to orange, and trinitrophenol is bright yellow.

Most of the classification tests for nitro compounds are color tests, making the use of standards for comparison necessary.

1. The Ferrous Hydroxide Test

The following equation shows the reaction that can be used as a classification test for the nitro group. It takes advantage of the ease of reduction of this group:

$$RNO_2 + 6\ Fe(OH)_2 + 4\ H_2O \rightarrow RNH_2 + 6\ Fe(OH)_3$$

reddish-brown
precipitate

The product, ferric hydroxide, is a reddish-brown precipitate. The speed with which this precipitate forms depends on the solubility of the nitro compound, but nearly all nitro compounds result in a positive test within 30 to 60 seconds. A greenish precipitate, which may darken slowly on standing, is a negative test. The success of this test depends on how well air and oxygen are excluded from the reagents while the test is being conducted. Ideally, therefore, this test should be carried out under in an inert atmosphere of nitrogen or helium.

2. The Zinc and Ammonium Chloride Test

This is a two-step test as shown by the following equations:

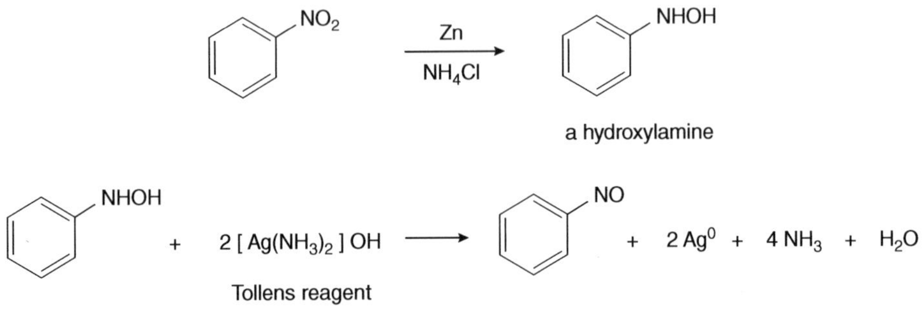

a hydroxylamine

Tollens reagent

Caution must be exercised with this test, since Tollens reagent gives the classic silver mirror with other readily-oxidizable substances (such as aldehydes). A preliminary Tollens test is therefore necessary.

3. Aromatic Nitro Compounds in Strong Base

If IR and NMR give evidence for both a nitro group and an aromatic ring, the unknown may be tested with sodium hydroxide solution to obtain further information. Nitrophenols develop an intense yellow or orange color when dissolved in aqueous base—probably due to the formation of stable, highly conjugated phenoxide ions:

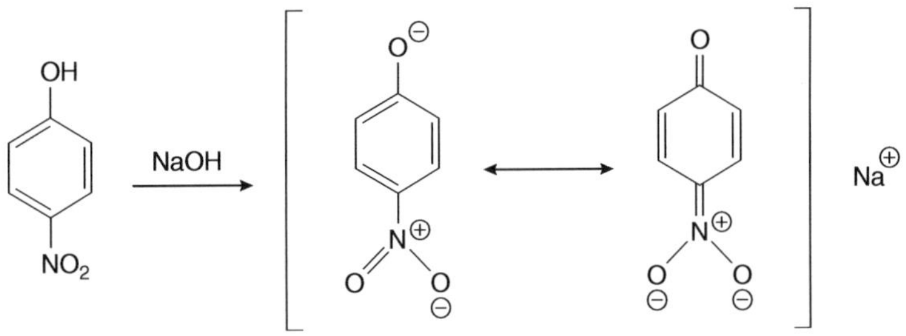

Because of the strongly electron-withdrawing properties of the nitro group, its presence activates an aromatic ring toward nucleophilic aromatic substitution. Nitroanilines and arylnitrohalides will therefore also react with hydroxide to produce a positive color test. The reactions will be slow, however, when compared to nitrophenol since a displacement reaction to produce a phenol must occur first.

Some polynitroaromatic compounds afford distinctive color tests when treated with strong base in acetone. For example, dinitro compounds tend to give a blue-purple color (except for *o*-dinitrobenzene, which produces almost no noticeable change). *p*-Dinitrobenzene turns greenish-yellow, 2,4-dinitroaniline is brick red, and trinitroaromatic compounds tend to be dark red. Care must be exercised with tests of this nature. It is always a good idea to run the test on a known compound alongside the unknown for color comparison.

Experimental Procedures

The following tests should be carried out with **nitrobenzene**, a **nitrophenol**, and **p-dinitrobenzene**. The results should be recorded as positive or negative in table form in your laboratory notebook.

1. *The Ferrous Hydroxide Test*

This test will not be performed because of the requirement of a source of inert gas (N_2 or He).

2. *The Zinc and Ammonium Chloride Test*

Pretest: Place about 0.04 g of the compound to be tested in a *clean* test tube, and add 2 mL of *freshly prepared* Tollens reagent (see the Aldehydes and Ketones Experiment for the preparation of this reagent). Agitate the tube vigorously, and allow it to stand for 10 minutes. If no reaction is observed, place the tube in a 40°C water bath for 5 minutes. Continue only if the test is negative. (What does it mean if the test is positive?)

Dissolve 0.2–0.3 g of the compound in a mixture of 2 mL of water and 3 mL of ethanol. Add 0.7 g of zinc dust and 0.3 gram of ammonium chloride. Stir the mixture thoroughly, and heat it in a boiling water bath until it boils. As soon as the mixture boils, remove it from the heat, and let it stand for five to ten minutes. If the mixture does not settle sufficiently in this time to give a clear supernatant liquid, it must be gravity filtered. Remove the clear liquid from the solids with a disposable pipet, and transfer it to a clean, dry test tube. Add 2 mL of the *freshly prepared Tollens reagent*, and note the results.

3. *Testing Aromatic Nitro Compounds with Base*

In addition to the known test compounds listed earlier, you should also observe the reaction of *p*-nitroaniline and a trinitroaromatic compound in the following test:

Place 5 mL of 20% sodium hydroxide, 3 mL of ethanol, and one drop or 0.1 g of the nitro compound into a test tube and shake vigorously. Compare the tests with a blank as follows: mix 5 mL of water, 3 mL of ethanol, and one drop of nitrobenzene and shake.

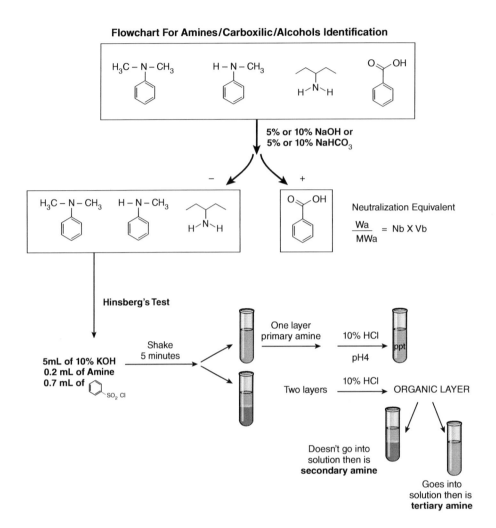

Figure 19-3. *Flowchart for Amines/Carboxylics/Alcohols Identification.*

Part 5: Carboxylic Acids and Esters

CARBOXYLIC ACIDS

Carboxylic acids are the acids of organic chemistry. The carboxyl group is readily deprotonated ($pK_a \approx 5$) because of the stability of the resulting conjugate base, the carboxylate ion.

Carboxylic
acid

Carboxylate ion

The boiling point of acetic acid is 30° higher than that of ethanol, an alcohol with the same molecular weight, because the acid is much more highly associated than the alcohol by two hydrogen bonds:

Aliphatic acids with up to eight carbons are liquids with pungent, unpleasant odors.

Carboxylic acids are more acidic than phenols. An indication of whether a water-insoluble compound is a carboxylic acid or a phenol can be determined by a simple solubility test. While both acids and phenols are soluble in dilute sodium hydroxide, only carboxylic acids will dissolve in dilute sodium bicarbonate with liberation of carbon dioxide. The reason for this difference in solubility in sodium bicarbonate solution is that carboxylic acids are more acidic than carbonic acid and therefore undergo deprotonation with bicarbonate anion as well as with all stronger bases. When water-soluble carboxylic acids dissolve in sodium bicarbonate solution, carbon dioxide is evolved. These solubility tests, therefore, also serve as classification tests. Phenols give positive color tests with ferric chloride and have distinctly different infrared absorptions from carboxylic acids.

The simplest and most informative way to characterize a carboxylic acid is to determine its **neutralization equivalent**. The neutralization equivalent of an organic acid is the same as its equivalent weight. It can be defined as *the number of grams of acid that correspond to one equivalent of hydrogen ions*. This value can be determined by titration of the carboxylic acid with a standardized sodium hydroxide solution. The molecular weight of the acid is obtained from the neutralization equivalent by multiplying that value by the number of carboxyl groups in the molecule.

$$\text{Neutralization equivalent} = \frac{\text{weight of sample in grams}}{\text{equivalents present}}$$

$$\text{equivalents of acid} = \text{equivalents of base}$$

$$\text{equivalents of base} = \text{mL of base used} \times \frac{1\,\text{L}}{1000\,\text{mL}} \times \text{Normality of the base}$$

To identify an unknown carboxylic acid, the following information should be obtained: the results of pH and solubility tests, the melting point or boiling point, the neutralization equivalent, and the melting point of one derivative.

Silver Nitrate Test

The silver nitrate test is useful for identifying carboxylic acids. The silver nitrate forms a precipitate of the silver salt of the carboxylic acid (as shown in the reaction below). Alkyl halides can also react with $AgNO_3$ to give the silver halide precipitate; however, the halide salts are not soluble in nitric acid.

Experimental Procedures

Test **acetic acid, benzoic acid, benzilic acid** and ***p*-chlorophenol** according to the procedures given below, and record the positive or negative results in table form in your notebook.

1. **The Solubility Test**

   Test the solubility of the compound in water, 5% sodium bicarbonate solution, and 5% sodium hydroxide solution by adding two drops or 0.1 g of the unknown to 5 mL of the reagent solution. Test the results of the water solubility with pH paper, and record the approximate pH of the solution.

2. **Neutralization Equivalent**

   NOTE: *It is only necessary to perform this test with one of the test acids (use benzoic acid).*

   Weigh out ≈0.2 gram of the carboxylic acid *to four decimal places* (use the analytical balance) into a 250 mL Erlenmeyer flask. Dissolve the sample in 50 mL of deionized water. If the substance is only partly soluble in water, add 95% ethanol, one mL at a time, until all of the sample is in solution. Add 3 drops of phenolphthalein indicator, and titrate with *standardized 0.1 N NaOH (normality given to 4 decimal places)* to a very faint, pink endpoint. Record the mL of base required, and the normality of the base.

3. Silver Nitrate Test

In a dry test tube, dissolve 4–5 drops of a liquid sample (or 50 mg of a solid sample) in 95% ethanol. Add 2 mL of a 2% solution of $AgNO_3$ (in 95% ethanol). Swirl around and look to see if any precipitate forms. If precipitation occurs, then add 5% HNO_3 and observe whether or not the precipitate dissolves (alkyl halide) or stays a precipitate (carboxylic acid). Record your results.

ESTERS

Esters are difficult to identify as a separate class. The presence of a carbonyl group in the infrared spectrum and negative solubility and chemical tests for other carbonyl-containing functional groups generally indicate an ester. In general, infrared and NMR spectra are the most useful tools in the identification of esters.

The primary reaction of esters is their base-promoted hydrolysis (called **saponification**), which affords the original carboxylic acid and an alcohol:

The acid and the alcohol can be separated and identified as described for –COOH and –OH, and the structure of the ester thus determined. The **saponification equivalent** of the ester can be obtained directly by conducting the hydrolysis in a measured volume of standardized alcoholic sodium hydroxide solution. After saponification of an accurately weighed quantity of the ester, the solution of the resulting carboyxlate ion is titrated with standardized hydrochloric acid, using phenolphthalein as the indicator.

$$\text{saponification equivalent} = \frac{\text{weight of sample in mg/mL}}{(\text{mL} \times \text{N of the base}) - (\text{mL} \times \text{N of acid})}$$

The saponification equivalent for the ester of a monoprotic acid is equal to the molecular weight of the ester. Like the neutralization equivalent of a carboxylic acid, this procedure requires good quantitative skills.

A useful color test that can be performed to confirm that an unknown is an ester is the **ferric hydroxamate test**.

> **NOTE:** Phenols and compounds which enolize will give false positive tests and must first be eliminated as possibilities before the ferric hydroxamate test is conducted.

1. The Ferric Hydroxamate Test

The electron-deficient carbonyl carbon of an ester undergoes nucleophilic acyl substitution by a variety of nucleophiles, in this case hydroxylamine (NH_2OH).

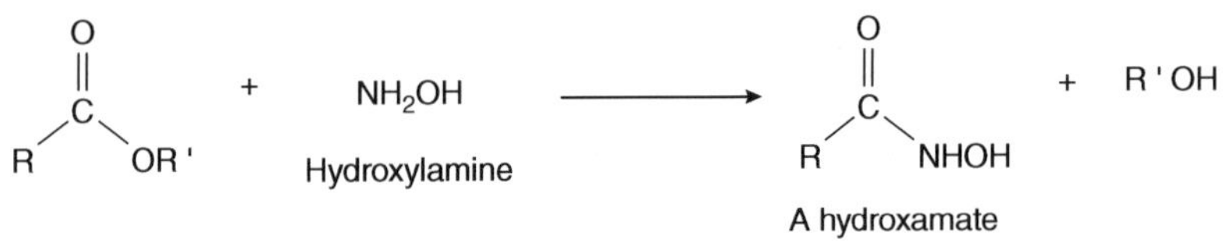

In the presence of ferric chloride reagent, the hydroxyl group of the hydroxamate results in the formation of a colored complex:

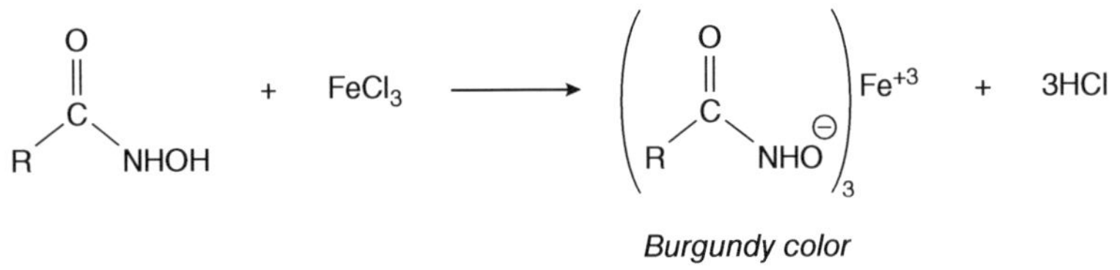

Burgundy color

Experimental Procedures

1. *The Ferric Hydroxamate Test*

Conduct this test on **phenol, salicylic acid,** and ***n*-butyl acetate.** Record the positive and negative results of both the pretest and the test itself in the form of a table so that comparisons can be easily made.

Pretest

Dissolve 1 drop or about 0.05 g of each of the three test compounds in 1 mL of ethanol. To these solutions, add 1 mL of 1 M hydrochloric acid and two drops of ferric chloride reagent. Examine a blank by mixing 1 mL of ethanol, 1 mL of 1 M HCl, and 2 drops of ferric chloride. Only a compound which produces a colorless to pale-yellow solution similar to the blank can be tested with confidence in the following procedure.

Test

Prepare a mixture of 3 mL of 0.5 M ethanolic hydroxylamine hydrochloride and 1 mL of 6 M sodium hydroxide, and divide it equally among three small test tubes. Add 1 drop or 0.05 g of each test compound to a test tube containing the reagent. Heat the test tubes in a hot water bath until the solutions boil. Remove the test tubes from the bath, and allow them to cool for a minute before adding 2 mL of 1 M hydrochloric acid to each tube. If any of the solutions becomes cloudy, add ethanol dropwise until the cloudiness just disappears. To each tube, add 2 drops of ferric chloride solution, and observe the color produced. If the color is only momentary, add additional ferric chloride reagent until a color persists. Compare the results of the pretest with this true test for the ester. An ester should produce a deep burgundy color.

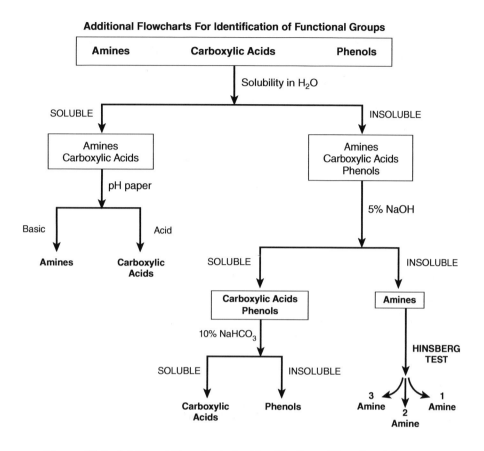

Additional Flowcharts For Identification of Functional Groups

Figure 19-4. *Additional Flowcharts for Identification of Functional Groups—*
Amines, Carboxylic Acids, Phenols.

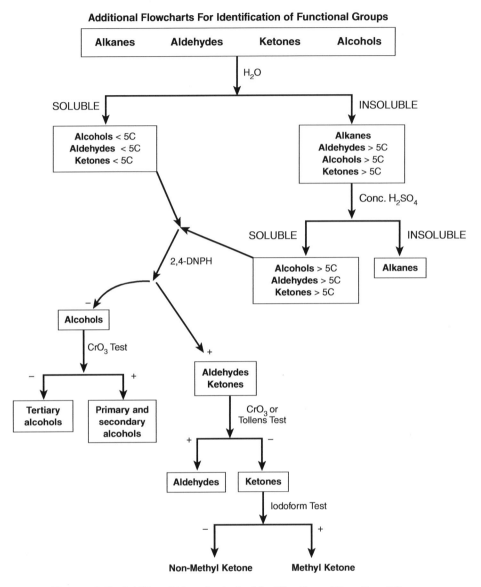

Additional Flowcharts For Identification of Functional Groups

Figure 19-5. *Additional Flowcharts for Identification of Functional Groups—Alkanes, Aldehydes, Ketones, Alcohols.*

CHAPTER 20

I Preparation of Derivatives

By following the procedures thus far, you should now have either pinpointed the identity of your unknown or have greatly narrowed down the number of possibilities. In order to complete the identification, you must prepare one or two solid derivatives. For the unknown to be a definite possibility, the melting point(s) of its derivative(s) must correspond to the values reported in the literature.

It is extremely important to obtain an accurate melting point of a derivative. Otherwise, you will probably reach the wrong conclusion regarding the identity of your unknown. Since the derivative that you prepare may be very impure, you must dry and recrystallize it before taking the melting point. Several recrystallizations may be required. Remember that the breadth of the melting point range will give you some insight as to the purity of your derivative.

It is very important to choose a derivative which will give you a clear-cut answer. For example, suppose your unknown is a liquid with a boiling point of 183–184°. Solubility, elemental analysis, and classification tests indicate that it is a primary amine. Looking at a table of derivatives, you find the following possibilities:

Compound	b.p.	m.p.	Benzamide	Picrate	Acetamide	Benzene-sulfonamide
Benzylamine	184	—	105	194	60	88
Aniline	184	—	163	198	114	112
4-Fluoroaniline	186	—	185	—	152	—
1-Phenylethylamine	187	—	120	—	57	—

Making the picrate derivative would not be a good idea since two of the possibilities do not have a picrate derivative listed, and the other two form picrates which have almost the same melting point.

You would also not want to make the acetamide derivative. Two of the possibilities form acetamide derivatives with almost the same melting point, so that a definitive decision between the two possibilities would not be possible.

Notice, however, that the benzamide derivatives of all four possibilities have widely separated melting points so that a definite decision could be made.

At this point in your investigation, a little bit of thinking and planning ahead of time can save you a lot of time and frustration in the lab.

Sometimes you will find several values listed for the same derivative. This results from more than one literature value being reported. In these cases, either value may be considered correct, and you should use whichever one corresponds more closely to the melting point of your derivative.

The literature values for the melting points of derivatives will be found in an appropriate table of derivatives. One such compilation is available at the end of this laboratory manual.

You are to prepare one or two derivatives of your unknown to prove its structure. A sample of the derivative(s) is to be handed in with your final report.

Remember, if you obtain a broad melting range for your derivative, you should recrystallize it again from a suitable solvent. Derivatives prepared or crystallized from water solutions should be dried thoroughly (for a few days) before a melting point is determined. However, to save time, small amounts may be dried by pressing them between several pieces of filter paper and spreading them out in the air.

The remainder of this section provides specific experimental procedures for the preparation of derivatives. The following table lists possible derivatives which may be prepared for each of the classes of compounds that you might be given as an unknown, along with the page number in this manual where the procedure is given:

Class of Compound	Derivative	Procedure Page
Alcohol	Phenyl- and α-Naphthylurethane	201
	Benzoate, *p*-Nitrobenzoate	201
	3,5-Dinitrobenzoate	202
Aldehyde	Phenylhydrazone	195
	2,4-Dinitrophenylhydrazone	196
	Semicarbazone	196
	Oxime	197
Amine	Benzenesulfonamide and *p*-Toluenesulfonamide	198
	Acetamide	198
	Benzamide	199
	Phenylthiourea	200
Carboxylic acid	Amide	203
	Anilide	203
	p-Nitrobenzyl ester	204
	Neutralization equivalent	202
Ketone	Phenylhydrazone	195
	2,4-Dinitrophenylhydrazone	196
	Semicarbazone	196
	Oxime	197
Phenol	α-Naphthylurethane	205
	Bromo derivative	205

| Procedures for the Preparation of Derivatives

ALDEHYDES AND KETONES

Phenylhydrazones

CAUTION: *Phenylhydrazine is carcinogenic. Handle it with care, and avoid direct contact.*

NOTE: *Phenylhydrazones decompose slowly in air. Preparation of this derivative should therefore be carried out as quickly as possible.*

Dissolve 100 mg of the aldehyde or ketone in a test tube. Add 4 mL of methanol and four drops of phenylhydrazine. Boil the mixture for 1 minute, and then add one drop of glacial acetic acid. Boil gently for 3 minutes. Add cold water drop by drop until the mixture becomes cloudy. Cool in an ice bath, and collect the crystals by suction filtration. Rinse them with 1 mL of water that contains a drop of acetic acid. Immediately recrystallize the phenylhydrazone by dissolving in a minimum amount of hot methanol and adding water until cloudiness appears. If necessary, cool and scratch the sides of the tube to induce crystallization. Collect the product by suction filtration, and wash it with a small amount of dilute, aqueous methanol. Dry the crystals by pressing between two layers of filter paper. Determine the melting point as soon as possible.

2,4-Dinitrophenylhydrazones

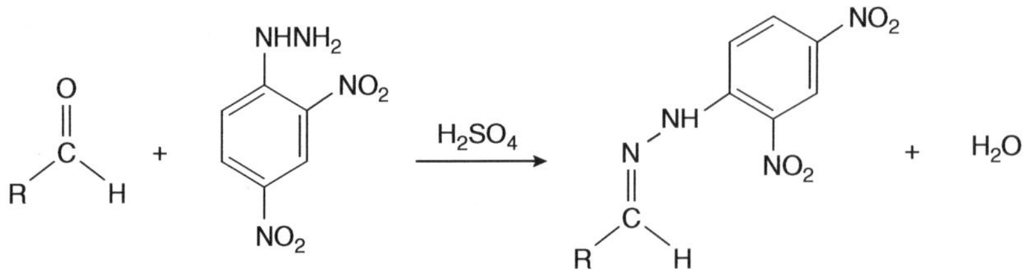

2,4-Dinitrophenyl-
hydrazine

2,4-Dinitrophenyl-
hydrazone

CAUTION: Phenylhydrazines are often carcinogenic. Handle them with care and avoid direct contact.

Prepare a solution of 0.5 g of the aldehyde or ketone in 20 mL of 95% ethanol. Add enough freshly prepared 2,4-dinitrophenylhydrazine solution to cause a small amount of precipitate to form, and allow the resulting mixture to stand at room temperature. The 2,4-dinitrophenylhydrazone will usually crystallize within 5 to 10 minutes. If no precipitate forms, allow the mixture to stand overnight.

Recrystallize the 2,4-dinitrophenylhydrazone by heating it in 30 mL of 95% ethanol on a hot water bath. If it dissolves immediately, slowly add water until cloudy or until a maximum of 5 mL of water has been added. If the 2,4-dinitrophenylhydrazone does not dissolve, slowly add ethyl acetate to the hot mixture until it dissolves. Allow the solution to stand at room temperature until crystallization is complete (about 12 hours).

NOTE: If there is any insoluble material remaining after the addition of the ethyl acetate, then the hot solution should be filtered through fluted filter paper before it is allowed to cool.

Semicarbazones

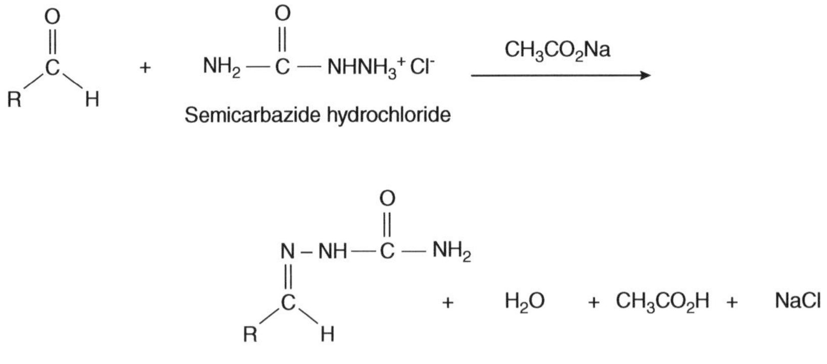

Semicarbazide hydrochloride

Semicarbazone

a. If the Aldehyde or Ketone Is Water Soluble

Place 1 mL of the liquid or 0.5 g of the solid aldehyde or ketone, 0.5 g of semicarbazide hydrochloride, and 1.0 g of sodium acetate in a test tube, and dissolve in 10 mL of water. Shake the mixture vigorously, place the test tube in a beaker of boiling water, and allow it to cool. Then place the test tube in a beaker of ice, and scratch the inside of the tube with a glass rod. Remove the crystals of the semicarbazone by filtration and recrystallize from water or 25 to 50% aqueous ethanol.

b.   *If the Aldehyde or Ketone Is Water Insoluble*

In a small beaker, dissolve 1 mL of the liquid or 0.5 g of the solid aldehyde or ketone in 10 mL of ethanol. Add water until the solution is faintly cloudy, and remove the cloudiness by adding a few drops of ethanol. Then add 1 g of semicarbazide hydrochloride and 1.5 g of sodium acetate. From this point, Procedure (a) is followed.

Oximes

NOTE: *Before attempting to prepare and use an oxime as a derivative, you should have a good idea of the identity of your unknown aldehyde or ketone. Oximes tend to be low melting and are often difficult to isolate and purify.*

Pyridine Method

CAUTION: *Pyridine is very toxic and has an extremely disagreeable odor. Avoid direct contact, and use it only in the hood.*

a. Reflux a mixture of 1 g of the aldehyde or ketone, 1 g of hydroxylamine hydrochloride, 5 mL of pyridine, and 5 mL of absolute ethanol for *two hours*. This will require that you set up a reflux apparatus consisting of a round-bottom flask, reflux condenser, and a heating mantle. Then remove the solvents by evaporation in a current of air *in the hood*. Triturate the residue thoroughly with 5 mL of cold water, and filter the mixture. The oxime is then recrystallized from methanol, ethanol, or an ethanol-water mixture (reserve a few crystals for seeding).

b. Dissolve about 0.5 g of hydroxylamine hydrochloride in 3 mL of water. Then add 2 mL of 10% sodium hydroxide solution and 0.2 g of the aldehyde or ketone. If the carbonyl compound is water insoluble, add just enough ethanol to the mixture to give a clear solution. Warm the mixture in a hot water bath for ten minutes. Then cool in an ice bath. In order to induce crystallization, scratch the sides of the test tube or flask with a glass rod. It may be necessary to add a few mL of distilled water to cause the oxime to separate. The product should then be recrystallized from water or dilute ethanol (reserve a few crystals for seeding).

Certain cyclic ketones, such a camphor, require an excess of alkali and a longer heating time. If a ketone does not yield an oxime by either Procedure (a) or (b), then treat it with 1 g of hydroxylamine hydrochloride, 4 g of potassium hydroxide, and 20 mL of 95% ethanol. Reflux the mixture for *2 hours*. This will require that you set up a reflux apparatus consisting of a round-bottom flask, reflux condenser, and a heating mantle. Then pour the reaction mixture into 150 mL of water. Stir the suspension and allow it to stand so that any unreacted ketone will separate. Filter the solution, acidify with hydrochloric acid, and allow it to stand so that the oxime will crystallize. Recrystallize the product from ethanol or an ethanol/water mixture (reserve a few crystals for seeding).

AMINES

Benzenesulfonamides and *p*-Toluenesulfonamides

CAUTION: *Benzenesulfonyl chloride and p-toluenesulfonyl chloride are lachryma-tors and are toxic. Avoid direct contact, and use them only in the hood.*

Place 0.2 g of the amine in a test tube, and add 0.5 mL of benzenesulfonyl chloride or 0.5 g of *p*-toluenesulfonyl chloride and 5 mL of 10% sodium hydroxide solution. Stopper the test tube, and shake it for 3 to 5 minutes. Carefully acidify the reaction mixture to pH 5 with 6 M HCl. Collect the precipitate by vacuum filtration, and wash it several times with a small amount of cold water.

Recrystallize the product by dissolving it in a minimum amount of hot 95% ethanol, adding hot water dropwise until the solution becomes cloudy, and then adding hot 95% ethanol dropwise until the solution clarifies. Cool and collect the product by vacuum filtration.

Acetamides

An acetamide

CAUTION: *Acetic anhydride is a toxic and irritating substance. Avoid breathing it and getting it on your skin.*

Prepare a solution of 0.5 g of the amine in 25 mL of 5% hydrochloric acid. Add small portions a 5% sodium hydroxide solution until the mixture becomes cloudy. Then, remove the cloudiness by adding 2 to 3 mL of 5% hydrochloric acid. Add a few small pieces of ice followed by 5 mL of acetic anhydride. Stir or swirl the mixture vigorously, and add—in one portion—sodium acetate solution (previously prepared from 5 g of sodium acetate trihydrate in 5 mL of water). If the product does not crystallize, chill the mixture overnight.

Recrystallize the acetamide from an ethanol–water mixture.

Benzamides

A benzamide

CAUTION: *Benzoyl chloride is a lachrymator, is toxic and a skin irritant. Avoid direct contact with it, and use it only in the hood.*

Pyridine, if used, is also very toxic and has an extremely disagreeable odor. Avoid direct contact, and use it only in the hood.

a. *If the Amine Is Water Soluble*

Place 4 or 5 drops of liquid amine or about 100 mg of solid amine in a test tube. Then add 20 drops of 10% NaOH solution and 10 drops of fresh benzoyl chloride. Stopper the test tube and shake it for ten minutes. Add 6 M HCl drop by drop until the pH is 7 to 8. Cool the mixture in an ice bath, and collect the crystals by vacuum filtration. Wash them with a small portion of cold water.

Recrystallize the benzamide by dissolving it in a minimum amount of hot 95% ethanol and adding hot water dropwise until the solution becomes cloudy. Then clarify the solution by the dropwise addition of hot 95% ethanol. Cool the solution and collect the crystals by vacuum filtration.

b. *If the Amine Is Water Insoluble*

Place 5 mL of pyridine, 0.5 mL of fresh benzoyl chloride, and 10 mL of toluene in a 50 mL round-bottom flask. Add 10 drops of the liquid amine or about 0.5 g of the solid amine, and reflux the mixture for 30 min. (This will require that you set up a reflux apparatus consisting of a round-bottom flask, reflux condenser, and a heating mantle.)

Pour the reaction mixture into a separatory funnel into which has been placed about 50 mL of water. Shake to hydrolyze any excess benzoyl chloride and to dissolve most of the pyridine. Separate the two layers, and wash the upper layer successively with 5 mL of water and then 5 mL of 5% sodium carbonate solution. Dry the upper layer over anhydrous magnesium sulfate. Filter off or decant the solution from the drying agent into a small Erlenmeyer flask. Remove the toluene by evaporation on a hot plate in the hood.

Recrystallize the benzamide from 95% ethanol, collect it by vacuum filtration, and dry it on a piece of filter paper.

The benzamides of some secondary amines are difficult to crystallize. If an oily liquid is produced, it should be scratched with a glass rod in the presence of a little solvent. It should then be recrystallized. Set aside a few crystals for seeding prior to recrystallization.

Phenylthioureas

A phenylthiourea

CAUTION: Phenyl isothiocyanate is an acute irritant. It should only be handled in the hood.

Place 3–4 drops of a liquid amine or 100 mg of a solid amine and 3–4 drops of phenyl isothiocyanate into a test tube, and shake vigorously for two minutes. If no reaction is observed to occur, heat the mixture for three minutes over a low flame.*

NOTE: Aliphatic amines usually react immediately; aromatic amines require heating. Place the reaction mixture in a beaker of ice until it solidifies. Crush the solid and wash it with hexane and 50% ethanol in order to remove any excess reactants. Recrystallize from 95% ethanol.

* *CAUTION: Use of a flame must always be done in the hood.*

ALCOHOLS

Phenyl- and α-Naphthylurethanes

ROH + [phenylisocyanate structure] N=C=O → [phenylurethane structure]

Phenylisocyanate   A phenylurethane

ArOH + [α-naphthylisocyanate structure] N=C=O → [α-naphthylurethane structure]

α–Naphthylisocyanate   An α–naphthylurethane

CAUTION: Phenylisocyanate and α-naphthylisocyanate are very toxic. Perform this reaction in the hood, and avoid direct contact with the reagent.

Place 1 g of the anhydrous** alcohol or phenol in a *dry* test tube, and add 0.5 mL of phenyl isocyanate or α-naphthylisocyanate. If a spontaneous reaction does not take place, warm the solution in a hot water bath for five minutes. Then cool it in a beaker of ice, and scratch the sides of the test tube with a glass rod to induce crystallization. Purify the urethane by dissolving it in 5 mL of hexane or carbon tetrachloride, filtering the hot solution, and cooling the filtrate in an ice bath. Collect the crystals by vacuum filtration and recrystallize from petroleum ether or dichloromethane.

** *Before proceeding with this procedure, dry a small amount of the unknown alcohol by placing it in a test tube with a small amount of anhydrous $MgSO_4$.*

CAUTION: Be suspicious of any derivative whose melting point is 241°, 268°, or 279°. These are the melting points of the ureas which are formed when the isocyanate reagent hydrolyzes.

Benzoates and *p*-Nitrobenzoates

ROH + [benzoyl chloride structure] C—Cl → [benzoate structure] C—OR + HCl

Benzoyl chloride   A benzoate

ROH + O_2N—[p-nitrobenzoyl chloride structure] C—Cl → O_2N—[p-nitrobenzoate structure] C—OR + HCl

p–Nitrobenzoyl chloride   A p–nitrobenzoate

CAUTION: Benzoyl chloride and p-nitrobenzoyl chloride are toxic; in addition, they are lachrymators and skin irritants. Avoid direct contact with them, and perform this reaction in the hood.

Pyridine is also toxic and has an extremely disagreeable odor. Avoid direct contact, and use it in the hood.

Dissolve 1 mL of the alcohol in 3 mL of anhydrous pyridine. Add 0.5 g of benzoyl or *p*-nitrobenzoyl chloride. After the initial reaction has subsided, warm the mixture over a low flame* for a minute, and pour it, with vigorous stirring, into 10 mL of water. Allow the precipitate to settle. Then decant the supernatant liquid. Thoroughly stir the residue with 5 mL of 5% sodium carbonate solution, and remove it by vacuum filtration. Recrystallize from ethanol.

*** CAUTION:** *Use of a flame must always be done in the hood.*

3,5-Dinitrobenzoates

$$ROH \quad + \quad \text{3,5–Dinitrobenzoyl chloride} \quad \longrightarrow \quad \text{A 3,5–dinitrobenzoate} \quad + \quad HCl$$

CAUTION: *3,5-Dinitrobenzoyl chloride readily hydrolyzes and is slowly converted into the 3,5-dinitrobenzoic acid if exposed to moist air. Therefore, check the purity of the reagent by determining its melting point. It should melt within 3°C of its literature value (74°C). If it has hydrolyzed, the melting point will usually be too high.*

About 0.5 g of 3,5-dinitrobenzoyl chloride is mixed with 2 mL of the alcohol in a test tube, and the mixture is boiled gently for five minutes. Then 10 mL of distilled water are added, and the solution is cooled in an ice bath until the product solidifies. The precipitate is collected on a filter, washed with 10 mL of a 2% sodium carbonate solution, and recrystallized from 5 to 10 mL of a mixture of ethyl alcohol and water of such composition that the ester will dissolve in the hot solution but will separate when the solution is cooled.

CARBOXYLIC ACIDS

Neutralization Equivalent

A simple way to characterize a carboxylic acid is to determine its **neutralization equivalent**. The neutralization equivalent of an organic acid is the number of grams of acid corresponding to one equivalent of hydrogen ions. This value can be determined by titration of the acid with standard base. The molecular weight of the acid can be obtained from the neutralization equivalent by multiplying the value thus obtained by the number of carboxyl groups in the molecule.

$$\text{Neutralization equivalent} = \frac{\text{weight of sample in grams}}{\text{equivalents present}}$$

$$\text{equivalents of acid} = \text{equivalents of base}$$

$$\text{equivalents of base} = \text{mL of base used} \times \frac{1 \text{ L}}{1000 \text{ mL}} \times \text{Normality of the base}$$

Weigh out a 0.2 g sample ($\pm$10%) of the acid to four decimal places (use the analytical balance) into a 125 mL Erlenmeyer flask. Dissolve the sample in 50 mL of 95% ethanol. If the sample is only partly soluble in water, add ethanol, one mL at a time, until all of the sample has gone into solution. Add 3 drops of phenolphthalein indicator, and titrate with a standard solution 0.1 N NaOH (normality given to four decimal places) to a very faint pink endpoint. Record both the mL of base required to reach the endpoint and the normality of the base.

Amides

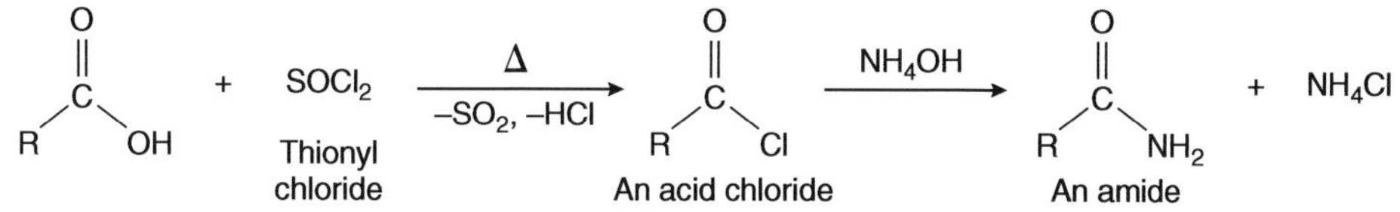

CAUTION: *Thionyl chloride is toxic, highly volatile, and reactive. It will cause serious burns if spilled on the skin. Handle it with care, and avoid direct contact. This reagent should be used only in the hood. This will avoid exposure to its fumes and to the SO$_2$ and HCl gas that are produced in the reaction.*

All parts of the following procedure must be carried out in the hood:

Set up a reflux apparatus consisting of a *dry* 25 mL round-bottom flask, reflux condenser, calcium chloride drying tube, and heating mantle. Place 1 g of the acid and 5 mL of thionyl chloride in the flask and reflux for 15 to 30 min. Pour the mixture cautiously into 15 mL of ice-cold, concentrated aqueous ammonia. Collect the precipitated amide by vacuum filtration.

Recrystallize the product by dissolving it in the minimum amount of hot 95% ethanol, adding hot water drop by drop until the solution becomes cloudy, then adding hot 95% ethanol drop by drop until the mixture is again clear. Cool the solution, and collect the crystals by vacuum filtration.

Anilides

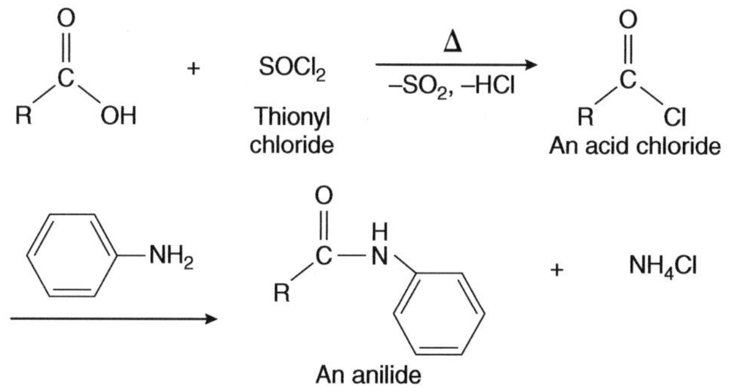

CAUTION: *Thionyl chloride is toxic, highly volatile, and reactive. It will cause serious burns if spilled on the skin. Handle it with care, and avoid direct contact. This reagent should be used only in the hood. This will avoid exposure to its fumes and to the SO$_2$ and HCl gas that are produced in the reaction.*

Set up a reflux apparatus consisting of a *dry* 25 mL round-bottom flask, reflux condenser, calcium chloride drying tube, and heating mantle. Place 0.5 gm of the carboxylic acid and 5 mL of thionyl chloride in the flask and reflux for 30 min.

Dissolve 1 g of aniline in 20 mL of toluene, and add this solution to the acid chloride mixture. Warm for 10 min.

Extract the reaction mixture successively with 5 mL of water, then with 5 mL of 5% HCl, then with 5 mL of 5% NaOH, and finally with 5 mL of water.

Dry the toluene layer over anhydrous magnesium sulfate. Filter off the drying agent, and pour the liquid into a small beaker. Evaporate the filtrate to dryness on a hot plate in the hood.

Recrystallize the product by dissolving it in the minimum amount of hot 95% ethanol, adding hot water dropwise until the solution becomes cloudy, and then adding hot 95% ethanol dropwise until the mixture clarifies. Cool the solution, and collect the crystals by vacuum filtration.

p-Nitrobenzyl Esters

A *p*-nitrobenzyl ester

CAUTION: p-Nitrobenzyl chloride is both a skin irritant and a lachrymator. Do not breathe it or get it on your skin. Work in the hood.

Add 1 gm of the carboxylic acid to 5 mL of water in a small flask and carefully neutralize it with 10% sodium hydroxide solution. Add a bit more of the acid until the solution is just acidic to pH paper. Add 10 mL of 95% ethanol and 1 g of *p*-nitrobenzyl chloride, and heat at reflux for 1 hr. (This will require that you set up a reflux apparatus consisting of a round-bottom flask, reflux condenser, and a heating mantle.) If a solid separates during the refluxing, it will be necessary to add a few additional mL of 95% ethanol. Allow the solution to cool. Recrystallize the ester from ethanol.

In preparing this derivative, make sure that the original reaction mixture is *not alkaline*. The presence of hydroxide causes hydrolysis of the *p*-nitrobenzyl chloride to *p*-nitrobenzyl alcohol.

PHENOLS

Phenyl and α-Naphthylurethanes

CAUTION: *Phenylisocyanate and α-naphthylisocyanate are very toxic. Perform this reaction only in the hood. Avoid direct contact with these reagents.*

Pyridine, if used, is very toxic and has an extremely disagreeable odor. Avoid direct contact, and use it only in the hood.

Thoroughly dry a small test tube in the oven, stopper it, and allow it to cool. Place 5 drops (or .200 mg) of the phenol, 1 drop of pyridine, and 5 drops of the isocyanate in the test tube, and immediately replace the stopper. If a spontaneous reaction does not take place, the solution may be warmed in a water bath maintained at 60–70° for five minutes. Cool the reaction mixture in an ice bath, and scratch with a glass rod if crystallization is not immediate. Purify the urethane by dissolving it in 5 mL of hot hexane, filtering the hot solution (gravity filtration through fluted filter paper), and cooling the filtrate in an ice bath. Collect the crystals by vacuum filtration, and recrystallize from petroleum ether or dichloromethane.

NOTE: *The hot filtration step is necessary to remove the insoluble ureas that will form if any traces of moisture were present.*

CAUTION: *Be suspicious of any derivative whose melting point is 241°, 268°, or 279°. These are the melting points of the ureas which are formed when the isocyanate reagent hydrolyzes.*

Bromination

CAUTION: *Bromine causes severe burns. Be careful not to get it on your skin. Bromine burns may be treated by flushing the affected area with plenty of water and applying a wet dressing of 10% sodium thiosulfate.*

A stock brominating solution may be prepared by dissolving 0.8 g of KBr in 5 mL of water and then adding 0.5 g of bromine.

Slowly add the brominating solution (dropwise), with shaking, to a solution of 1 g of the phenol dissolved in water, methanol, ethanol, or acetone. Add just enough of the brominating agent to impart a yellow color to the mixture. Then add about 50 mL of water, and shake the mixture vigorously to break up the lumps. Separate the bromo derivative by filtration, and wash the solid with a dilute solution of sodium bisulfite (to remove any excess Br_2). Recrystallize the derivative by dissolving it in a minimum amount of hot 95% ethanol, adding hot water dropwise until the solution becomes cloudy, and then adding hot 95% ethanol until the mixture is clear again. Cool the solution and collect the product by vacuum filtration.

Aryloxyacetic Acids

An aryloxyacetic acid

Add 1.5 g of chloroacetic acid to a mixture of 1 g of the phenol and 5 mL of 33% aqueous sodium hydroxide solution. Shake the mixture thoroughly, and add 1 to 5 mL of water if necessary to dissolve the sodium salt of the phenol. Place the test tube containing the reaction mixture in a beaker of boiling water for one hour. Then cool the solution, dilute it with 10 to 15 mL of water, acidify to pH 1–2 with dilute hydrochloric acid, and extract with 50 mL of ether. Wash the ether solution with 10 mL of cold water, and then shake with 25 mL of 5% sodium carbonate solution. Carefully acidify (CO_2 evolution!) the sodium carbonate solution with dilute hydrochloric acid, and collect the aryloxyacetic acid by vacuum filtration. Recrystallize from hot water.

The crystals are then collected on filter paper and recrystallized again from petroleum ether or dichloromethane.

Tables of Derivatives
of Selected Organic Compounds

Acids, Carboxylic (Liquids)					
Name of Compound	b.p.	Anilide	p-Toluide	p-Nitrobenzyl Ester	p-Bromo-phenacyl Ester
Formic	101	47	53	31	135
Acetic	118	114	147	78	85
Acrylic	140	104	141		
Propionic	140	103	124	31	63
Isobutyric	155	105	104		77
Methacrylic	163	87			
n-Butyric	163	95	72	35	63
Pivalic	164	129	120		76
Pyruvic	165d	104	109		
Crotonic (cis)	165d	102	132		82
Ethylmethylacetic	176	110	93		55
Isovaleric	176	109	109		68
Chloroacetic	185	134	120		105
α-Chloropropionic	186	92	124		
n-Valeric	186	63	70		75
2,2-Dimethylbutanoic	187	92	83		
Dichloroacetic	189	118	153		99
Diethylacetic	193	124	116	66	
Isocaproic	195	11	63		79
d,l-2-Methylpentanoic	196	95	81		
3-Methylpentanoic	197	87	75		
Tiglic	198	77	76	64	68
n-Caproic	205	95	75		72
α-Bromopropionic	205	99	125		

---

* Taken, in part, from: R.L. Shriner, R.C. Fuson, D.Y. Curtin, T.C. Morrill, *The Systematic Identification of Organic Compounds*, 6th Ed., John Wiley & Sons, 1980.

Acids, Carboxylic (Solids)				
Name of Compound	m.p.	Anilide	Amide	*p*-Nitrobenzyl Ester	*p*-Bromo-phenacyl Ester
Hexahydrobenzoic	30	142	86		
Capric	30	62	108		67
Levulinic	33	102	108	61	84
Pivalic	35	129	154		76
2-Phenylbutyric	42		86		
β-Chloropropionic	42		101		
Lauric	43	76	98		76
Tridecanoic	44	80	100		75
α-Bromoisovaleric	44		133		
β-Phenylpropionic (Hydrocinnamic)	48	92	82	36	104
α-Bromoisobutyric	49		148		
Bromoacetic	50	131	91	88	
γ-Phenylbutyric	52		84		
Myristic	54	84	102		81
Trichloroacetic	57	94	141	80	
Palmitic	62	90	106	42	86
Chloroacetic	63	134	120		105
Tiglic	64	77	76	64	68
Stearic	69	93	108		90
Crotonic (*trans*)	72	118	160	67	96
Phenylacetic	76	117	154	65	89
α-Hydroxybutyric	79	136	98	80	
α-Benzoylbutyric	87		149		
Dibenzylacetic	89	155	128		
o-Benzoylbenzoic	90	195	165	100	
Citraconic	91	175	187d	71	
Phenoxyacetic	96	99	101		148
Glutaric	97	224	174	69	137
o-Methoxybenzoic	100	131	128		113
Oxalic (hydrated)	101	257	419d	204	242d
o-Toluic	102	125	142	91	57
Pimelic	105	155			137
Azelaic	106	185	175	44	131
m-Toluic	110	125	97	86	108
p-Isopropylbenzoic	116	150	125		

Acids, Carboxylic (Solids), continued				
Name of Compound	**m.p.**	**Anilide**	**Amide**	**p-Nitrobenzyl Ester**	**p-Bromo-phenacyl Ester**
d,l-Mandelic	118	151	133	124	
m-Nitrophenylacetic	120		10		
Benzoic	121	160	128	89	119
3-Nitrosalicylic (hydrated)	125		145		
o-Benzoylbenzoic	126	195	165	100	
2,4-Dimethylbenzoic	127		179		
Maleic	130	187	153	89	168
Sebacic	133	198	210	72	147
d- or *l*-Mandelic	133		122		
trans-Cinnamic	133	153	147	116	145
α-Naphthylacetic	133	155	181		
Acetylsalicylic	135	136	138	90	
2,6-Dichlorobenzoic	139		202		
o-Chlorobenzoic	140	114	139	106	106
m-Nitrobenzoic	140	153	142	141	132
o-Nitrophenylacetic	141		161		
β-Naphthylacetic	142		200		
3-Nitrosalicylic	144		145		
Diphenylacetic	145	180	167		
o-Nitrobenzoic	146	155	174	112	107
p-Hydroxyphenylacetic	148		167		
o-Bromobenzoic	150	141	155	110	
Benzilic	150	175	154	99	152
Adipic	152	235	220	106	154
p-Nitrophenylacetic	152		198		207
2,5-Dichlorobenzoic	153		155		
Citric	153		210d	102	148
m-Bromobenzoic	155	146	155	105	
2,4,6-Trimethylbenzoic	155		188		
Salicylic	157	134	139	96	140
m-Chlorobenzoic	158	122	134	107	116
2,4-Dichlorobenzoic	160				
α-Naphthoic	162	161	205		135
2,3-Dichlorobenzoic	164				
3,4-Dimethylbenzoic	164		130		

Acids, Carboxylic (Solids), continued				
Name of Compound	m.p.	Anilide	Amide	p-Nitrobenzyl Ester	p-Bromo-phenacyl Ester
4-Nitrophthalic	165	192	200d		
Mesitylenic	166		133		
d,l-Phenylsuccinic	167	122 (di)	211 (di)		
d- or l-Tartaric	169	180	195	163	216
3,5-Dinitrosalicylic	173	181	197		
p-Toluic	181	140	158	104	153
4-Chloro-3-nitrobenzoic	182	131	156		
2,4-Dinitrobenzoic	183		203	142	158
p-Anisic	184	168	162	132	152
β-Naphthoic	185	173	195		
d-Camphoric	187	203	192	66	
Hippuric	187	208	183	136	151
m-Iodobenzoic	187		186	121	128
Succinic	188	226	242	88	211
3-Nitroanisic	190	163			
m-Nitrocinnamic	199		196	174	173
2-Chloro-3, 5-dinitrobenzoic	199				
m-Hydroxybenzoic	201	155	170	106	176
3,5-Dinitrobenzoic	202	234	183	157	
Phthalic	206d	169	149	155	153
Vanillic	207			140	
p-Hydroxybenzoic	213	202	162	198	191
3-Nitrophthalic	218	234	201	189	
2,4,6-Trinitrobenzoic	220d		264d		
5-Nitrosalicylic	227	224	225		
Piperonylic	229		169		
o-Nitrocinnamic	240		185	132	141
p-Nitrobenzoic	241	217	201	168	137
p-Chlorobenzoic	242	194	179	129	
p-Bromobenzoic	251	197	189	139	
p-Iodobenzoic	265	210	217	141	147
p-Nitrocinnamic	285		204	186	
Isophthalic	300		280	215	186
Terephthalic	300	337		263	225
Fumaric	302		314		151

Alcohols (Liquids)				
Name of Compound	b.p.	α-Naphthyl Urethane	Phenyl Urethane	3,5-Dinitro-benzoate
Methyl alcohol	66	124	47	107
Ethyl alcohol	78	79	52	93
Isopropyl alcohol	83	106	88	122
t-Butyl alcohol	83	101	136	142
3-Buten-2-ol	96			
Allyl alcohol	97	109	70	48
n-Propyl alcohol	97	80	51	74
s-Butyl alcohol	99	97	65	75
t-Pentyl alcohol	102	71	42	117
Isobutyl alcohol	108	104	86	86
Methyl isopropyl carbinol	113	112	68	76
n-Butyl alcohol	116	71	63	64
Diethyl carbinol	116	71	48	97
2-Pentanol	119	76		61
2-Methyl-2-pentanol	121		239	72
Ethylene glycol monomethyl ether	125	113		
1-Chloro-2-propanol	127			83
3-Methyl-3-pentanol	128		50	
s-Butyl carbinol	128	97		62
Ethylene chlorohydrin	129	101	51	92
4-Methyl-2-pentanol	131	88	143	65
3-Hexanol	135			77
n-Pentyl alcohol	138	68	46	46
Cyclopentanol	140	118	132	115
Triethyl carbinol	142			
Acetoin	145			
Hydroxyacetone (acetol)	146			
2-Methyl-1-pentanol	148	76		51
2-Ethyl-1-butanol	149			51
2-Bromoethanol	150	86	76	
3-Heptanol	156			
Di-*n*-propyl carbinol	156	80		64
n-Hexyl alcohol	156	59	42	58
Cyclohexanol	160	128	82	112

Alcohols (Liquids), continued				
Name of Compound	**b.p.**	**α-Naphthyl Urethane**	**Phenyl Urethane**	**3,5-Dinitro-benzoate**
2-Heptanol	160	54		49
Trimethylene chlorohydrin	161d	76	38	77
2-Methylcyclohexanol	165	155	103	
Furfuryl alcohol	170	129	45	80
Ethylene glycol monobutyl ether	171			
Pinacol	172		215	130
4-Methylcyclohexanol	174	160	125	
3-Methylcyclohexanol	175	122	96	
Diisobutyl carbinol	175			47
n-Heptyl alcohol	176	62	68	29
1,3-Dichloro-2-propanol	176	115	73	
Trimethylene bromohydrin	176d	73		
2-Methyl-1,2-propanediol	178		141	84
Tetrahydrofurfuryl alcohol	178		61	32
2-Octanol	179	63	114	
2,2-Dibromoethanol	181			96
Cyclohexylcarbinol	182	110		
2,3-Dichloro-1-propanol	182	93	73	
2,3-Butanediol	183		201	
2-Ethyl-1-hexanol	184	61	34	
Propylene glycol	188		153	
Butyroin	190			61
n-Octyl alcohol	192	66	74	
Diethylene glycol monomethyl ether	193			
5-Nonanol	194			
2-Methyl-2,4-pentanediol	196			169
Ethylene glycol	197	176	157	
Linalool	197	53	65	43
2-Nonanol	198	56		
Diethylene glycol monoethyl ether	202			95
Methylphenylcarbinol	203	106	94	112
Benzyl alcohol	205	134	78	
1,3-Butanediol	208	184		44
2-Decanol	211	69		

Alcohols (Liquids), continued				
Name of Compound	b.p.	α-Naphthyl Urethane	Phenyl Urethane	3,5-Dinitro-benzoate
3-Chloro-1,2-propanediol	215 (d)			52
n-Nonyl alcohol	215	65	62	164
Trimethylene glycol	216	164	137	
Benzyl dimethyl carbinol	216			
m-Tolylcarbinol	217	116		
Methyl-*p*-tolylcarbinol	219		96	
β-Phenethyl alcohol	219	119	79	108
2,3-Dibromo-1-propanol	219		77	
Ethylphenyl carbinol	219	102		
dl-α-Terpineol				
Geraniol	224	47		62
n-Decyl alcohol	231	71	60	57

Alcohols (Solids)			
Name of Compound	m.p.	α-Naphthyl Urethane	Phenyl Urethane	3,5-Dinitro-benzoate
Lauryl alcohol	24	80	74	60
p-Methoxybenzyl alcohol	25		94	
Cinnamyl alcohol	33	114	90	121
Pinacol	35		215	
α-Terpineol	35	147	112	78
o-Tolyl carbinol	36		79	
(–)-Menthol	42	128	111	
Cetyl alcohol	50	82	73	66
Neopentyl alcohol	53	100	144	
Piperonyl alcohol	58		102	
Benzhydrol	69	136	140	
o-Nitrobenzyl alcohol	74			
Phenacyl alcohol	86			129 (p-nitro-benzoate)
p-Nitrobenzyl alcohol	93			
Benzoin	133	140	165	see ketones
(–)Cholesterol	148	160	168	
Triphenylcarbinol	162			
Benzopinacol	186			
(+)-Borneol	208	132	138	137 p-nitrobenzoate

Aldehydes (Liquids)					
Name of Compound	b.p.	Oxime	Semi-carbazone	Phenyl-hydrazone	2,4-Dinitro-phenyl-hydrazone	p-Nitro-phenyl-hydrazone
Acetaldehyde	21	47	162	63, 99	147, 168	129
Propionaldehyde	50	40	89, 154	liq	154	124
Acrolein	52		171	52	165	
Isobutyraldehyde	64		125	liq	182	132
n-Butyraldehyde	74		104	liq	122	92
Pivalaldehyde	75	41	190		209	119
Isovaleraldehyde	92	48	107	liq	123	101
α-Methyl-butyraldehyde	93		103		120	
Chloral	98	56			131	
n-Valeraldehyde	130	52			106	
Crotonaldehyde	103	119	199	56	190	184
α-Ethylbutyraldehyde	116		96		134	
Caproaldehyde	128	51	106		104	
Heptaldehyde	156	57	109		108	73
Furfural	161	89, 74	202	97	229	
Octaldehyde	171	60	101		106	80
Bromal	174	115				
Benzaldehyde	179	35	222	158	237	
Phenylacetaldehyde	194	103	156	58	121	
Salicylaldehyde	196	57	231	142	252d	
m-Tolualdehyde	199	60	213	84	211	
o-Tolualdehyde	200	49	208	101	195	
p-Tolualdehyde	204	79, 110	221	114	239	
Citronellal	206	liq	82		77	
o-Chlorobenzalde-hyde	208	78	225	86	207	
m-Chlorobenzalde-hyde	208	70	228	134	256	
Caproaldehyde	209	69	102		104	

Aldehydes (Solids)					
Name of Compound	m.p.	Oxime	Semi-carbazone	Phenyl-hydrazone	2, 4-Dinitro-phenyl-hydrazone
Palmitaldehyde	34	88	109		108
α-Naphthaldehyde	34	90	221	80	
Phenylacetaldehyde	34	99	156	63	121
o-Iodobenzaldehyde	37	108	206	79	
Piperonal	37	110	230	100	266d
o-Methoxybenzaldehyde	38	92	215		253
Stearaldehyde	38	89	119		110
o-Aminobenzaldehyde	40	135		221	
o-Nitrobenzaldehyde	44	102	256	156	250d
3,4-Dimethoxybenz-aldehyde	44	95	177	121	265
Lauraldehyde	45	78	106		106
p-Chlorobenzaldehyde	47	110	230	127	270
Chloral hydrate	53	56	90d		131
2,3-Dimethoxy-benzaldehyde	54	99	231	138	264d
Phthalaldehyde	56			191	
p-Bromobenzaldehyde	57	157 (s) 111 (a)	228	113	
m-Iodobenzaldehyde	57	62	226	155	
m-Nitrobenzaldehyde	58	120	246	124	293d
β-Naphthaldehyde	60	156	245	206d	270
2,4-Dimethoxybenzalde-hyde	69	106			
2,4-Dichlorobenzaldehyde	71	136			
Vanillin	80	117	229	105	271d
m-Hydroxybenzaldehyde	105	88	199	131	260d
p-Nitrobenzaldehyde	106	129	221	159	320d
p-Hydroxybenzaldehyde	115	72	224	177	280d
3,5-Dihydroxybenzalde-hyde	157		223		

		Amines, Primary (Liquids)				
Name of Compound	b.p.	Benzene-sulfonamide	Benzamide	p-Toluene-sulfonamide	Phenyl-thiourea	Acetamide
Ethylamine	19	58	71	63	106	
Isopropylamine	33	26			101	
t-Butylamine	46		134		120	101
n-Propylamine	49	36	84	52	63	
Allylamine	56	39		64	98	
sec-Butylamine	63	70	76	55	101	
Isobutylamine	69	53	57	78	82	
n-Butylamine	77		42		65	
Isopentylamine	95			65	102	
1,2-Diaminopropane	102		139	192	103	
n-Pentylamine	104				69	
Ethylenediamine	116	168	172	249	160	102
n-Hexylamine	128	96		40		77
Cyclohexylamine	134	89	104	149		148
1,3-Diaminopropane	136	96	126	147	148	
n-Heptylamine	155					75
1,4-Diaminobutane	160					168
1,5-Diaminopentane	178	119				148
n-Octylamine	180					
Aniline	183	112	114	160	103	154
Benzylamine	184	88	60	105	116	156
α-Phenylethylamine	185		57	120		
β-Phenylethylamine	198	69	114	116		135
o-Toluidine	199	124	112	143	108	136
m-Toluidine	203	95	65	125	114	94
l-Menthylamine	205		145	156		135
o-Chloroaniline	207	129	87	99	105	156
4-Amino-1,3-dimethylbenzene	212	128	133	192		133
m-Ethylaniline	215					
2-Amino-1,3-dimethylbenzene	216		176	168		204
o-Ethylaniline	216		111	147		
p-Ethylaniline	216		94	151		104

Amines, Primary (Liquids), continued						
Name of Compound	**b.p.**	**Benzene-sulfonamide**	**Acetamide**	**Benzamide**	***p*-Toluene-sulfonamide**	**Phenyl-thiourea**
5-Amino-1,3-dimethylbenzene	220	136	144			153
2,3-Dimethylaniline	222		136	189		
o-Bromoaniline	229		99	116		146
o-Phenetidine	229	102	79	104		137
m-Chloroaniline	230	121	72	120		124

		Amines, Primary (Solids)				
Name of Compound	m.p.	Benzene-sulfonamide	Acetamide	Benzamide	p-Toluene-sulfonamide	Phenyl-thiourea
m-Iodoaniline	27		119	157	128	
o-Bromoaniline	31		99	116		146
p-Amino-*N*-methyl-aniline	36		63	165		
p-Amino-N,*N*-diethylaniline	41		130	228		
1,6-Diaminohexane	42	154 (di)		155 (di)		
p-Toluidine	45	120	153	158	117	141
2-Aminobiphenyl	45		119	86		
4-Amin*o*-1,2-dimethylbenzene	49	118	99		154	
2,5-Dichloroaniline	50		132	120		
α-Naphthylamine	50	167	159	160	157	165
2-Amino-3,5-dichlorotoluene	50		186			
4-Aminobiphenyl	53		171	230		
o-Iodoaniline	56		109	139		
p-Anisidine	57	95	127	154	114	154
2-Amino-5-bromotoluene	59		156			
p-Iodoaniline	62		183	222		153
m-Phenylenediamine	63	194	191	240	172	
2,4-Dichloroaniline	63	128	145	117	126	
3-Aminopyridine	64		133	119		
p-Bromoaniline	66	134	167	204	101	148
p-Chloroaniline	70	121	179	192	95	152
o-Nitroaniline	71	104	92	94		142
4-Amino-2-nitrotoluene	77	160	148	172	164	145
2,4,6-Trichloroaniline	77		204	174		
2,4-Dibromoaniline	79		146	134	134	
3-Amino-6-chloro-toluene	83		91			
2,6-Dibromoaniline	83		210			
Ethyl *p*-aminobenzoate	89		110	148		
2-Methyl-6-nitroaniline	91		157	167		
2-Methyl-3-nitroaniline	95		158			
6-chloro-2,4-dibromo-aniline	95		227	192		

Amines, Primary (Solids), continued						
Name of Compound	m.p.	Benzene-sulfonamide	Acetamide	Benzamide	*p*-Toluene-sulfonamide	Phenyl thiourea
2,4-Diiodoaniline	96			181		
8-Nitro-1-naphthyl-amine	97	194	191			
2-Amino-4-methyl-pyridine	98	103	114			
2,4-Diaminotoluene	99	178	224	224	192	
o-Phenylenediamine	102	185	185	301	201	
2,6-Diaminotoluene	105		203			
p-Aminoacetophenone	106	128	167	205	203	
2-Amino-4-nitrotoluene	107	172	150			
β-Naphthylamine	112	102	132	162	133	129
m-Nitroaniline	114	136	155	155	138	160
4-Amino-3-nitrotoluene	116	102	96	148	166	
1,4-Diamino-naphthalene	120		303	280		
p-Aminobenzophenone	124		153	152		
Benzidine	127	232	317	352	243	
o-Tolidine	129		314	265		
2-Amino-5-nitrotoluene	130	158	198	174	174	
3-Amino-6-nitrotoluene	135		102			
2,6-Dinitroaniline	138		197			
p-Phenylenediamine	140	247	304	300	266	
2-Amino-5-nitronaph-thalene	144		186	182		
1-Amino-2-nitronaph-thalene	144		199	175		
p-Nitroaniline	147	139	210	199	191	
p-Aminoacetanilide	162		304			
4-Amino-2,6-dinitro-toluene	169					
o-Aminophenol	174	141	201	182	139	146
2,4-Dinitroaniline	180		120	202	219	
2,4,6-Trinitroaniline	190	211	230	196		
1,5-Dinitro-2-naphthylamine	191		201		182	

Amines, Secondary (Liquids)					
Name of Compound	**b.p.**	**Benzene-sulfonamide**	**Benzamide**	**p-Toluene-sulfonamide**	**Phenyl-thiourea**
Methylethylamine	35				
Diethylamine	55	42	42	60	34
Diisopropylamine	86				
Pyrrolidine	89			123	
Piperidine	105	93	48	96	101

Name of Compound	**b.p.**	**Benzene-sulfonamide**	**Acetamide**	**Benzamide**	**p-Toluene-sulfonamide**	**Phenyl-thiourea**
Di-*n*-propylamine	110	51				69
Diallylamine	111					
d,l-2-Methylpiperidine	116			45	55	
d,l-3-Methylpiperidine	126					
Morpholine	130	118		75	147	136
Diisobutylamine	139	55	86			113
Di-*n*-butylamine	160					86
N-Methylbenzylamine	185				95	
Diisoamylamine	187					72
N-Methylaniline	192	79	102	63	94	87
N-Ethylbenzylamine	199				50	
N-Ethylaniline	205		54	60	87	89
Di-*n*-pentylamine	205					72
N-Methyl-*m*-toluidine	206		66			
N-Methyl-*o*-toluidine	207		55	66	120	
N-Methyl-*p*-toluidine	208	64	83	53	60	89
N-Isopropylaniline	213		39			
N-Methyl-*o*-chloro-aniline	214					
N-Ethyl-*p*-toluidine	217	66		40	70	
N-Ethyl-*o*-toluidine	218	62		72	75	
N-Ethyl-*m*-toluidine	221			72		
N-Isobutylaniline	231					
Tetrahydroisoquino-line	233	154	46	129		

Amines, Secondary (Solids)						
Name of Compound	**m.p.**	**Benzene-sulfonamide**	**Acetamide**	**Benzamide**	***p*-Toluene-sulfonamide**	**Phenyl-thiourea**
Tetrahydroquinoline	20	67		75		
N-Benzylaniline	37	298	119	58	107	103
o-Nitro-*N*-methyl-aniline	37		70			
N-Methyltribromo-aniline	39		101			
Indole	52			68		
Diphenylamine	54	124	101	180	141	152
4-(*N*-Ethylamino)-3-nitrotoluene	59				127	
N-Phenyl-α-naphthyl-amine	62		115	152		
m-Nitro-*N*-ethylaniline	65		89			
N-Methyl-*m*-nitroaniline	66	83	95	156		
Di-*p*-Tolylamine	79		85	125		
4-(*N*-Methylamino)-3-nitrotoluene	84		64			
N-Ethyl-*p*-nitroaniline	96		118	98	107	
p-Tolyl-β-naphthylamine	103		85	139		
Piperazine	104	282	134	191	173	
N-Ethyl-2,4-dinitroaniline	113					
p-Nitro-*N*-methylaniline	152	120	153	111		
N-Methyl-2,4-dinitroaniline	176					
Carbazole	243		69	98		

Ketones (Liquids)					
Name of Compound	b.p.	Oxime	Semi-carbazone	Phenyl-hydrazone	2,4-Dinitro-phenyl-hydrazone	p-Nitro-phenyl-hydrazone
Acetone	56	59	187	42	126	152
Methyl ethyl ketone	80		146		117	129
Methyl vinyl ketone	80		141			
Isopropyl methyl ketone	94		113		117	
Methyl *n*-propyl ketone	102	58	110		144	117
Diethyl ketone	102	69	139		156	141
Pinacolone	106	74	157		125	139
Isobutyl methyl ketone	119	58	135		95	
Chloroacetone	119		164d			
α,α-Dichloroacetone	120		163			
Diisopropyl ketone	125	34	160		95	
n-Butyl methyl ketone	129	49	122		106	88
Mesityl oxide	130	49	164		203	134
Cyclopentanone	131	56	205	50	142	154
Bromoacetone	136	36				
2-Methylcyclopenta-none	139		184			
Di-*n*-propyl ketone	145		133		75	
Acetoin	145		185	243d	315	
Hydroxyacetone	146	71	196	106	129	
n-Pentyl methyl ketone	151		127	207	89	73
Cyclohexanone	155	90	166	77	162	146
Di-*sec*-butyl ketone	162		84			
2-Methylcyclohexanone	163	43	195		137	
Diisobutyl ketone	168	210	121		92	
3-Methylcyclohexanone	169		180		155	
4-Methylcyclohexanone	169	37	199		130	
n-Hexyl methyl ketone	172		122		58	92
Methyl cyclohexyl ketone	180	60	177		140	154
Cycloheptanone	181	23	163		148	137
Di-*n*-butyl ketone	187		90		41	
Acetophenone	200	59	198	105	250	
l-Menthone	207	59	187	53	146	
Isophorone	214	76	191	68	130	

Ketones (Liquids), continued					
Name of Compound	**b.p.**	**Oxime**	**Semi-carbazone**	**Phenyl-hydrazone**	**2,4-Dinitro-phenyl-hydrazone**	**p-Nitro-phenyl-hydrazone**
2-Hydroxyacetophe-none	216	117	210	110		
Methyl o-tolyl ketone	216	61	206		159	
Propiophenone	218	53	174		191	
Methyl m-tolyl ketone	220	57	200		207	
Isobutyrophenone	222	61, 94	181	73	163	
Pulegone	224		174		142	
Isovalerophenone	225	74	210		240	
Carvone	225	72	142	106	193	
Benzyl ethyl ketone	226		135			
Methyl p-tolyl ketone	226	86	205	94	260	
m-Chloroacetophenone	228	88	232	176		
Phenyl n-propyl ketone	230	50	184	200		
p-Chloroacetophenone	232	95	201	114	231	

Ketones (Solids)				
Name of Compound	m.p.	Oxime	Semi-carbazone	Phenyl-hydrazone	2,4-Dinitro-phenyl-hydrazone
Benzyl methyl ketone	27	70	198	87	156
Phorone	28	48	186		
p-Methylacetophenone	28	88	205	96	258
2-Hydroxy-acetophenone	28	117	210	110	
Dihexyl ketone	33				
α-Naphthyl methyl ketone	34	139	229	146	
Dibenzyl ketone	34	125	146	120	100
p-Chloro-propiophenone	36	63	176		
p-Methoxy-acetophenone	38	87	198	142	220
Benzalacetone	41	115	187	157	223
1-Indanone	42	146	233	135	258
α,α'-Dichloroacetone	45		120		
Benzophenone	48	141	164	137	239
p-Bromoacetophenone	51	128	208	126	230
Methyl β-naphthyl ketone	53	145	237	176	262
Phenyl p-tolyl ketone	54	154, 136	122	109	200
Deoxybenzoin	60	98	148	116	204
p-Methylbenzophenone	60	154	122	109	202
Benzalacetophenone	62	73, 75	168, 180	120	245
p-Methoxybenzophe-none	62	116, 138	132, 90	180	
Laurone	69	40	179		
Dihydroxyacetone	72	84			278
Dibenzoylmethane	78		205		
p-Chlorobenzophenone	78	163		106	185
m-Nitroacetophenone	77	132	257	128	228
Fluorenone	83	195	234	151	283
Di-p-tolyl ketone	92	163		100	229
3-Hydroxyacetophe-none	96		195		

Ketones (Solids), continued					
Name of Compound	**m.p.**	**Oxime**	**Semi-carbazone**	**Phenyl-hydrazone**	**2,4-Dinitro-phenyl-hydrazone**
Dibenzalacetone	112	144	190		180
Acenaphthenone	121	175		90	
Benzoin	133	151	206d	106	245
p-Hydroxybenzophe-none	135	152	194	144	244
2,4-Dihydroxyaceto-phenone	147	199	214	159	
p-Hydroxypropiophe-none	148				229
4,4'-Dichlorobenzo-phenone	148	135			
d,l-Camphor	178	118	235		164
(+)-Camphor	179	118	237	233	177

Phenols (Liquids)				
Name of Compound	**b.p.**	**α–Naphthyl-urethane**	**Bromo derivative**	**Aryloxy-acetic acid**
o-Chlorophenol	175	120		145
Phenol	180	133	Tribromo..95	99
o-Cresol	190	142	Dibromo..56	152
o-Bromophenol	195	129	Tribromo..95	143
3-Chloro-*p*-cresol	197			108
p-Cresol	202	146	Dibromo..49	136
m-Cresol	202	128	Tribromo..84	103
Guaiacol	205	118	Tri-bromo..116	121
o-Ethylphenol	207			141
2,4-Dichlorophenol	209		Bromo..68	138
2,4-Dimethylphenol	212			

Phenols (Solids)				
Name of Compound	**m.p.**	**α–Naphthyl-Urethane**	**Bromo Derivative**	**Esters**
2,4-Dimethylphenol	26	135		Benzoate..38
Guaiacol	28	118	Tribromo..116	Benzoate..57
o-Ethoxyphenol	28			Benzoate..31
o-Cresol	31	142	Dibromo..56	3,5-Dinitro-benzoate..133
m-Bromophenol	32			
2-Bromo-4-chlorophenol	34			Benzoate..100
3-Nitro-*p*-cresol	34			Benzoate..102
p-Cresol	36	146	Tetrabromo..108	Benzoate..71
2,4-Dibromophenol	36		Tribromo..95	Benzoate..97
Phenol	42	133	Tribromo..95	Benzoate..68
p-Chlorophenol	43	166		Benzoate..93
2,4-Dichlorophenol	43		Bromo..68	Benzoate..97
o-Nitrophenol	45	113	4,6-Dibromo..117	3,5-Dinitro-benzoate..142
6-Chloro-3-methylphenol	46			Benzoate..31
p-Ethylphenol	47	128		Benzoate..60
5-Chloro-*o*-cresol	48			Benzoate..71
3,5-Dibromo-*p*-cresol	49			Benzoate..95
2,6-Dimethylphenol	49	176	Bromo..79	3,5-Dinitro-benzoate..159
Thymol	50	160	Bromo..55	Benzoate..32
2-Chloro-3-methylphenol	50			Benzoate..56
Hydroquinone monomethyl ether	53			Benzoate..87
3,5-Dibromo-*o*-cresol	57			*p*-Nitro-benzoate..137
2,3-Dichlorophenol	57		Dibromo..90	
2,5-Dichlorophenol	59			Benzoate..69
p-Bromophenol	63	169	Tribromo..95	Benzoate..102
3,4-Dimethylphenol	63	142	Tribromo..171	Benzoate..58
2-Chloro-5-hydroxy-toluene	66	154		Benzoate..86
2,4,6-Trichlorophenol	67	188		Benzoate..70
3,5-Dichlorophenol	68		Tribromo..189	Benzoate..55
2,4,5-Trichlorophenol	68			Benzoate..93
3,5-Dimethylphenol	68		Tribromo..166	3,5-Dinitro-benzoate..195

Phenols (Solids), continued				
Name of Compound	**m.p.**	**α–Naphthyl-Urethane**	**Bromo Derivative**	**Esters**
2,4,6-Trimethylphenol	69		Dibromo..158	
2,5-Dimethylphenol	74	173	Tribromo..178	Benzoate..61
2,3-Dimethylphenol	75			
α-Naphthol	94	152	2,4-Dibromo..105	Acetate..46 Benzoate..119
p-tert-Butylphenol	95		Bromo..50	Benzoate..83
2,4,6-Tribromophenol	95	153	Tetrabromo.120	Acetate..82
m-Nitrophenol	97	167	Dibromo.. 91	Benzoate..95
Catechol	104	175	Tetrabromo..192	Diacetate..63
1,2-Dihydroxynaphthalene	108			Acetate..106
Resorcinol	110		2,6-Dibromo..112	Dibenzoate..117
3-Hydroxy-2,4,6-trinitrotoluene	110			Acetate..135
p-Nitrophenol	114	151	2,6-Dibromo..142	Acetate..81
2,4-Dinitrophenol	114		6-Bromo..118	Acetate..72
p-Hydroxybenzaldehye	115		3,5-Dibromo..181	Benzoate..90
Picric Acid	122			Acetate..76
β-Naphthol	122	157	Bromo..84	Acetate..70
Pyrogallol	133		Dibromo..158	Triacetate..165
2,4-Dinitronaphthol	138			Benzoate..174
1,8-Dihydroxynaphthalene	140			Diacetate..148
2,4-Dinitroresorcinol	148			
p-Phenylphenol	165			Acetate..89
Hydroquinone	169	247	Dibromo..186	Diacetate..123
1,4-Dihydroxynaphthalene	176	220		Diacetate..128
Pentachlorophenol	190			Acetate..150
Phloroglucinol	218		Tribromo..151	Triacetate..105

UNKNOWN 1

Name	
Panther ID	Date

Preliminary Identification (20 points)

You have been given an unknown compound. In the first part of this lab, you will examine the physical properties, solubility, and elemental analysis of the unknown. Fill out the information below as best as possible. A successful determination of the functional group in your unknown compound is dependent upon the following examinations. You will be graded on how accurate and diligent you perform. At the final step you must predict two potential functional groups that your compound might contain AND explain your reason for choosing that functional group. DO NOT SEPARATE/TEAR THE PAGES OF THE UNKNOWN EXAMINATION!

Unknown number _____

1. ***Physical properties*** *(5 points)*

    Solid or liquid _____

    Color _____

    Ignition test

       Flammability _____

       Manner of melting _____

       Odor of gases _____

    Beilstein test (testing for halogens) _____

    Melting point _____

    Boiling point _____

2. ***Solubility*** *(5 points)*

H_2O	5% or 10% HCl	5% or 10% NaOH	5% or 10% $NaHCO_3$

    Reactivity with H_2SO_4 _____

3. *Elemental Analysis (Sodium Fusion)* (5 points)

Nitrogen	Chlorine	Bromine

4. *Predictions of functional group present and reasoning why* (5 points)

1. _____

   _____

   _____

   _____

   _____

2. _____

   _____

   _____

   _____

   _____

UNKNOWN 1

Name			
Panther ID		Date	

Final Examination (20 points)

In the second part of the unknown lab you will first isolate which functional group (of the two you predicted) is present. You will then prepare 2 derivatives of your unknown in an attempt to identify the actual unknown compound. Fill out the information below as best as possible. You will be graded on how accurate your answers are for your unknown. At the final step you must identify your unknown compound. DO NOT SEPARATE/TEAR THE PAGES OF THE UNKNOWN EXAMINATION!

Unknown number ____________

1. *Narrowing your functional group* *(5 points)*

Give the details as to what tests you did to narrow your functional group (including whether it's 1°, 2°, or 3° as for amines/alcohols).

____

____

____

____

____

____

2. *Derivative #1* *(5 points)*

Reagent used ______________________________

Names of predicted derivative compound(s) and their melting point(s)__________

____

____

____

____

Experimental melting point ______________________________

3. **_Derivative #2_** *(5 points)*

Reagent used _____

Predicted derivative compound _____

Predicted derivative compound melting point _____

Experimental melting point _____

4. **_Name your unknown compound_** *(5 points)*

_____

UNKNOWN 2

Name	
Panther ID	Date

Preliminary Identification (20 points)

You have been given an unknown compound. In the first part of this lab, you will examine the physical properties, solubility, and elemental analysis of the unknown. Fill out the information below as best as possible. A successful determination of the functional group in your unknown compound is dependent upon the following examinations. You will be graded on how accurate and diligent you perform. At the final step you must predict two potential functional groups that your compound might contain AND explain your reason for choosing that functional group. DO NOT SEPARATE/TEAR THE PAGES OF THE UNKNOWN EXAMINATION!

Unknown number _____

1. **Physical properties** *(5 points)*

   Solid or liquid _____

   Color   _____

   Ignition test

       Flammability   _____

       Manner of melting   _____

       Odor of gases   _____

   Beilstein test (testing for halogens) _____

   Melting point _____

   Boiling point _____

2. **Solubility** *(5 points)*

H_2O	5% or 10% HCl	5% or 10% NaOH	5% or 10% $NaHCO_3$

   Reactivity with H_2SO_4 _____

3. *Elemental Analysis (Sodium Fusion)* *(5 points)*

Nitrogen	Chlorine	Bromine

4. *Predictions of functional group present and reasoning why* *(5 points)*

1. _____

2. _____

UNKNOWN **2**

Name	
Panther ID	**Date**

Final Examination (20 points)

In the second part of the unknown lab you will first isolate which functional group (of the two you predicted) is present. You will then prepare 2 derivatives of your unknown in an attempt to identify the actual unknown compound. Fill out the information below as best as possible. You will be graded on how accurate your answers are for your unknown. At the final step you must identify your unknown compound. DO NOT SEPARATE/TEAR THE PAGES OF THE UNKNOWN EXAMINATION!

Unknown number _____

1. ***Narrowing your functional group*** *(5 points)*

   Give the details as to what tests you did to narrow your functional group (including whether it's 1°, 2°, or 3° as for amines/alcohols).

   _____

   _____

   _____

   _____

   _____

   _____

2. ***Derivative #1*** *(5 points)*

   Reagent used _____

   Predicted derivative compound _____

   Predicted derivative compound melting point _____

   Experimental melting point _____

3. ***Analysis of ¹H NMR: match the peaks with your functional group*** *(5 points)*

On the attached ¹H-NMR spectrum draw the structure of your compound and assign the peaks to the appropriate protons.

4. ***Name your unknown compound*** *(5 points)*

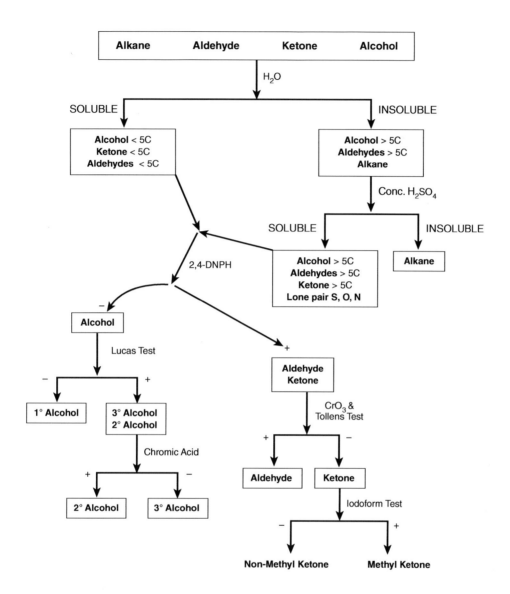

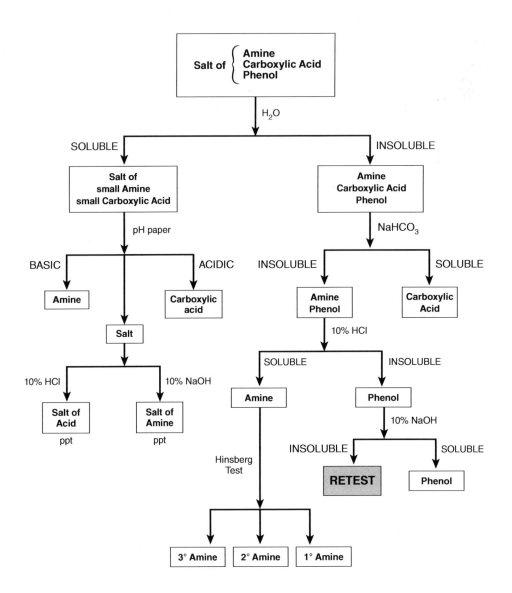